Wherever I Wander

Wherever I Wander

JUDITH AZRAEL

IMPASSIO
PRESS

Grateful acknowledgment is made to the following publications in which portions of this book have appeared: *Atlanta Review:* "Antiparos"; *Buddhism Now:* "Sleeping Like the Buddha" and "Walking the Footpath of the Buddha"; *Calliope:* "Death of Three"; *Crab Apple Review:* "Leaving the Island"; *The Diarist's Journal:* "Greek Island Sketchbook"; *Fearless Mountain:* "Sleeping Like the Buddha"; *Harvard Review:* a selection from "House in the Olive Grove"; *Poets & Writers Magazine:* a short selection from "Thursdays"; *Rosebud:* selections from "Southeast Asia Sketchbook"; *Shenandoah:* "Thursdays"; *The Sun:* "Winning and Losing"; *Western Humanities Review:* "Counting Cats"; *The Yale Review:* "Journey"; *An Inn Near Kyoto: Writing by American Women Abroad* (an anthology published by New Rivers Press): "Southeast Asia Sketchbook"; and *Travelers' Tales Greece: True Stories* (an anthology): a short excerpt from "Counting Cats."

Front Cover Serigraph: *Path to Serenity* by Lewis Spaulding
Back Cover Serigraph: *Serenity* by Lewis Spaulding
Author Photo: Satiko
Design: Magrit Baurecht

Library of Congress Control Number: 2004101282

ISBN: 0-9711583-4-7

Impassio Press, LLC
P.O. Box 31905
Seattle, WA 98103
www.impassio.com

Contents

Acknowledgments

There are so many people to whom I would like to express my gratitude. I think first of the Buddhist monks and nuns who have graced my life with their purity and wisdom. And my thoughts roam to Greece and the countless people there who welcome me with friendship and open-heartedness. And I would like to offer thanks to my editor and publisher, Olivia Dresher, for her warm support and sensitivity.

Wherever I Wander

PART I

Surrender

Death of Three

I found, a few days ago, an animal washed up on the beach just below my cabin. From a distance I could not tell what it was . . . perhaps a coyote or a dog. And I must confess that for a moment it seemed it might be a mythical creature there amidst the gleaming beach stones. The blue inland sea was strangely calm that day and in the distance those uncountable islands appearing and disappearing in the mist.

As I drew nearer I saw that it was a deer . . . a doe . . . her head flung back in surrender. Her large ear, stiffly raised, was etched in black and lined with soft white. The slender graceful legs ending in ebony dancer's hooves. I have heard that deer sometimes swim from island to island. And sometimes drown.

This death did not seem sad. Not here in this place where eagles soar. A few days earlier I had seen a young eagle doing astonishing flips in the air. I was alone on the beach and the eagle alone in the sky. And then it was gone. I stood there transfixed for a long time. No this death did not seem sad . . . the lovely unscarred deer stretched out beneath the sky. At sunset I brought down a sketchbook and drew its graceful curves. The tide was beginning to sweep in . . . cool water lapping at the body of the deer.

That night I woke again and again . . . piled wood into the woodstove . . . stepped out for a few moments under the bright dome of stars. The tide was still high. I wondered if the deer would be washed out to sea.

I arose at dawn. The tide had withdrawn leaving a wide stretch of stones. The deer looked stranded and matted and forlorn there on the dry rocky shore. No vultures or eagles or coyotes had found it . . . had taken it for their food. I avoided the beach that morning, having breakfast instead around the bend on the grassy cliffs. I could have stayed another day at the cabin, my solitary and peaceful retreat. But instead I took the ferry that weaved and swayed away over that bright blue water. I went back to town.

I drove back thinking of another death that happened when I lived by another sea . . . a lovely orange cat, a stray, who moved in with us trying the easy life, carpets and cat food and the like, but kept all her hunting habits. At dawn when I was sleepy and unsuspecting I would let her in. She would enter carrying a live mouse or an occasional mole. She would sit all day in the sunlight on a wooden deck where fuchsias grew abundantly and hummingbirds danced suspended in the bright air. She had a perch above the humming-birds there on the deck and could leap down and catch them in a flash. And although I believe in the cycles of nature, I somehow couldn't bear to see those beings of pure color and motion and light trapped in the jaws of my cat. I would look out of the window and see feathers peeking out of the corners of her mouth. And I would run out, pry her mouth open and the bird would soar away miraculously unharmed. The cat didn't seem to mind. I never saw her eat one. Perhaps she thought it wasn't worth it—not much content to a hummingbird. I think it was their amazing quickness that fascinated her . . . that lured her to match it with her own.

When she wasn't catching hummingbirds, she perched aesthetically, gracefully on some lofty perch . . . the roof or the high rafters of the house overlooking the sea. A photographer friend from Toronto

asked if he could take her back home with him for his model. But
I steadfastly refused.

Then one day I noticed she looked awful . . . weak and sick. And I
realized she hadn't evidenced her fiercely independent spirit for
some time, realized I had known this and not known it for awhile.
I was concerned. So were my children. We took her to the vet.

Alas the town had changed also. No longer did Andre the hippie vet
live out in the woods and charge whatever people could afford.
Once he had sewn up a dog of ours and just for good measure
attached a large safety pin. The dog recovered in leaps and bounds.
But now we had an appointment in an air-conditioned office
where a neatly dressed receptionist inquired about the name of the
pet and its previous medical record and its age.

But it is death I am writing about . . . death and discovery and even
joy. The vet declared that the cat had leukemia, had no red blood
cells left and would die in a very few days. He gave me several
choices: to have her put to sleep, to give her some vitamin shots
which had about a one percent chance of helping her, or elaborate
blood transfusions and hospitalization that would be prohibitively
expensive and had little chance of saving her. The children and I
talked sadly and we all agreed. We took her home with her vitamin
shots and some sticky protein in a tube that I was supposed to
squeeze in her mouth a few times a day.

And then began a strange vigil that lasted about a week. The children
went to school each day. And on a deck by the sea I tried squeezing
the sticky stuff in my cat's mouth. She spit it out, all over her lovely
fur. After that she learned to clamp her jaws so tightly I could not
budge them. I fried her tiny pieces of liver in butter and served
them up. I gave her warmed milk and bits of browned hamburger.
She grew weaker and I would carry her to her bowl, carry her in the

hopes that she would grow more alert with change of locale. But she would stand there wobbly and sticky-furred, half sleeping half waking. She would just stand there. I held food up to her mouth. She wouldn't even lick. And after awhile I would carry her away.

I would carry her to the deck and there in the sunlight amidst her beloved hummingbirds and shining fuchsia I would hold her on my lap, press my face against her fur and catch the scent of meadow grass still lingering there. And I would plead with her not to die.

But mostly I was guardian of these her last days . . . taking her with me from room to room so I could keep watch over her. The vitamins began to produce their biochemical change. Occasionally she would lick at the food I kept placing before her. Once or twice I saw her weakly but steadfastly cleaning her fur and one night my daughter called joyously from her room that the cat had begun to purr. But the shots wore off and the vet agreed there was no hope, no reason for giving them to her once again. All progress stopped. And then the rapid downhill slide.

I am getting now closer to the point. One night I held the cat in my arms and we stared into each other's eyes. Hers looked merciless. I was shaken by their intensity. The look went on and on . . . and I was the one to finally turn away.

What had I learned? It is difficult to put into words. I saw that I had been willing the cat to live . . . willing her by my vigilance, by my attention, by the fierceness of my desire. I thought about her eyes, about those tightly clamped jaws from a creature with so little strength. That evening I gave up. I let the cat go.

I found the cat dead the next morning. When the children came home we buried her in the meadow. No grave markers except the bareness of that earth. And no words.

What happened next was that I felt released. I felt a peacefulness enter my being that was deep and complete. I walked the bluffs for days, watching the sea spill and dance against the beach. I visited the rock wall where cormorants hid their sleek black bodies in the shadows of the rock. I wrote poetry . . . a long series of rapturous poems called *The Luminous Mountain*. I did yoga by my large sea windows. The silence . . . the solitude seemed sacred. I stopped answering the telephone.

What had I learned. Perhaps something about responsibility . . . that mine was simpler and lighter in this universe than I had ever imagined. But I think it was more . . . I know it was more . . . deeper and more mysterious, my truth. Something of the shape the curve of breath.

My grandmother died when I was twenty-three. (Though, oddly, my father sometimes asks me in a sad and puzzled tone, Judith, do you remember your grandmother? Yes I remember my grandmother, her beauty her dignity . . . yes father . . . how safe and loved I felt with her.) Because I was living a thousand miles away, because I had a baby and because of reasons I cannot fathom, no one informed me of her death until after the funeral. Otherwise I would have been there.

When the call came I cried. Sad surprised tears. Though it would be years until I learned to truly sorrow, to enter that dark wave that would rock me and pummel me and hold me and then spill me cleansed and wet and shining back into the light. Whenever I thought of my grandmother she seemed alive. I had to be careful not to make a slip, not to ask for news of her. I dreamed of her often and in my dreams she still lived. Though I had some photographs of her I sometimes looked at, photographs taken some months before her death, and in them she looked pale and transparent as a ghost. Finally the dreams ceased and years flowed by. And then I

dreamed of her again . . . dreamed she was cradling me in her arms
and we were laughing we were weeping we were sobbing. We were
saying goodbye.

There are times when each day seems a miracle of brightness and of
joy. It was a time like that when I wrote a letter to my mother and
father, a note sent on an impulse from my heart. And in it I thanked
them for giving me my birth. On the beach below my cabin a few
days ago there was a dead deer, lying stretched on the sand . . . with
its lovely and graceful form. And there for a moment in the sunlight
in the silence with the sea barely whispering against the shore, I
gave thanks for being present at this death.

Leaving the Island

I write this for you, mother, because your heart is tender. And because there is little that any of us can do to ease another's longing. We plan our days and feel we know what will come next. But some days go their own way and surprise us. Some are cruel and stunning as the stroke that canceled all our plans. You have learned to walk again and your arm and your hand have grown strong. You are across the country where the summer days are sultry. And I am standing on a rocky shore with the wind blowing and a seal pup in my arms.

First I will tell you about this morning. It is slow and peaceful. I am moving away in a few days and my car is already packed. All the last chores have been done. I wander down the road along the sea and stop to weed in John Brown's garden. His wife died last summer and the garden is in need of care. He's away and I've always wanted to work in this garden. I move among the bright oriental poppies and pull up grasses and wayward dandelions. The garden is across the road from the sea. I work and watch the fishermen getting their boats readied for opening day. Friends stop by to chat. Someone tells me there is a seal pup on the beach. And so the weeding never does get finished.

I find a small group of people are gathered around the seal. This is what I learn. It was found four days ago and part of its umbilical cord was still attached. Some girls have tried feeding it with a baby bottle but the seal couldn't suck on the nipple. Yesterday someone saw it struggle to the water and swim out of sight. But it is back now and it is hungry. Its eyes are luminous and gentle and its fur is soft.

I drive to the shore to buy some baby formula and to try to reach some animal clinics or aquariums for advice. It is Sunday and I get only answering services. They insist there is no emergency. I return to the beach with a baby bottle and some infant formula. The seal doesn't respond at all when the nipple is placed in its mouth. Instead it sucks eagerly at my hand. I pour the milk again and again over my hand. The seal sucks and most of the milk runs into useless puddles on the stones. A tiny amount ends up inside the seal. At dusk I leave reluctantly with a dim hope that the mother will appear sometime during the night. I think about taking the seal home with me but I do not dare. Weeks later I will wonder again and again at that lack of daring. But the fact remains. I do not dare. I leave it there in the wind that is growing cold. Its light gray fur is hardly visible amidst the driftwood and the gray beach stones.

Early the next morning I am back. It takes a long time to find the seal. It is nestled beneath a driftwood log. It is hungry. It sucks my hand eagerly and for the first time I lift it. It presses its soft mouth against mine, still searching for food. It nuzzles my cheeks and my neck. It seems to fit naturally in my arms, curving itself easily into position. I am covered with seal spit and any distance I had hoped to maintain has disappeared.

A fisherman has some herring and we mince it into tiny pieces and place it in the seal's mouth. It struggles gently as we pry open its mouth. Inside are tiny teeth but they don't seem to know what to do with fish. The pieces of herring just stay there in its mouth though perhaps some get swallowed inadvertently. We carry the seal to the water, thinking it may be important that it spend some time there. But it climbs hastily back up the beach looking wet and cold. I place my hand inside its front flipper and it curls around my fingers. Now and then it makes soft mewing sounds. It is clear that the mother didn't return during the night to feed it. And the feeding I am doing isn't nearly enough.

During the day others stop by to check on the seal. People try calling for help. Someone has the number of a seal hotline whose purpose is to help stranded seals. But we can't get through. The instructions we do get are simple enough. Leave the seal alone. Its mother will return. I don't believe it. It has been too long and the seal is dehydrated. And suddenly I'm frightened. Many of the people I've spoken to seem to feel it is futile and ultimately heart-breaking to get involved with an abandoned seal. One couple on the island raised one only to have it shot by fishermen. Another woman was threatened with a federal fine. And I am leaving in two days. How will I ever be able to leave.

Are these my mothering instincts that have been awakened after a long sleep. It is a bodily feeling. Skin and blood and veins and muscles are all coming alive. I feel like a dry streambed after the first spring rain. I feel like a woman who has just given birth, every inch of her body, thighs and arms and breasts that are usually silent now sighing and pulsing with life. I brush my mouth against the seal's soft fur. And it sucks with its warm eager mouth on my hands. My clothes and my hair and my skin are bathed in milk and smooth saliva and tiny bits of fish.

This is a story of many words, mother, though usually my words are few. I find I am reluctant to leave anything out. Last night after I left the seal I saw Mark. We rode the ferry to the mainland. We had dinner on the deck of a small café. It faced the water and we watched the sun setting over the islands. We have said goodbye many times and in many ways but this time I will not summon him back to me, back to confusion and pain.

Sometimes in the summer on the island it rains for weeks, a harsh cold rain that consumes the fleeting summer days. And then the sun returns. The day is suddenly warm and the sea turns a deep irresistible blue. We are not fools. Yet how easily we forget the darkness. Oh mother how easily we forgive the rain.

I leave the seal in the late afternoon. I leave because I cannot bear its helplessness. I go to find Charlotte to tell her about the seal. She knows already. She tells me a man named Jannik took it home last night and fed it and slept with it in his arms. This morning he returned it to the beach.

I call Jannik and we meet for the first time on the beach in the darkness with a cold wind blowing. He brings milk for the seal. It is a special formula suggested to him by a marine biologist. We find the seal and carry it into Jannik's van to feed it. He has cared for orphan lambs and calves and has devised a way to feed the seal. While it sucks at my hand he squirts warm milk from a dropper into the corner of its mouth. Our hands meet and overlap as we feed the seal. Its soft mouth sucks hungrily. The air smells of milk and fur and our clothes are damp but the seal swallows most of the milk. And Jannik tells me about sleeping all through the night with the seal and how its body nestled against his.

We place the seal near a driftwood log for the night. I go back to my cabin to get pillows and blankets. We've decided to spend the night in the van watching to see if the mother seal returns. Perhaps this way we can convince the authorities that the pup has truly been abandoned. I lie stretched out in the front seat and Jannik in the back. The seal is now only a pool of darkness beside the driftwood. The wind blows and waves crash into shore. I gaze out into the night wondering if the mother seal will come. And Jannik and I talk sleepily.

He has come back to the island after many years. He will be running a buyer boat and buying salmon from the Indians and the white fishermen. There will be long days and nights on the water on a small boat floating among islands. We talk of New England and his life there. A fire recently consumed everything he owned. He says it left him feeling humble as a monk. Ah we know, mother, about humbleness and how simple our lives and our dreams can suddenly become. I was there when you moved your fingers for the first time, moved them an infinitesimal distance to touch my own. Tonight it is a seal I am dreaming of, hoping it will emerge from a vast and dark sea. Jannik and I go on talking and watching and the hours slip by and the wind goes on blowing. Waves rush in to shore. Then we take turns dozing and watching until it begins to grow light.

At dawn he leaves for work. And I feel my departure loom close. Tomorrow is the day I will leave the island. But how can I leave the seal. Today one of its shining eyes seems clouded. It is hungrier and thinner. It opens its mouth to the air in a new and pitiful way.

I go down to the café to use the telephone. I call the seal hotline and am given the number of a woman named Jessica who runs an animal shelter. Jessica answers the phone. She has heard about the seal and has been concerned about it. She is certain the mother has abandoned it and that the seal needs immediate help. She will make arrangements with a small island airline to transport the seal and will call me back. I wait nervously for the phone to ring. And when it does a little later it is Jessica. Can you be at the airport in an hour she asks. Yes I reply.

Tom is sitting at the counter, a big quiet man with long hair and rough clothes. He agrees to help me take the seal to the airport. We drive to the beach and find the seal. I place it in Tom's arms. He looks surprised and touched and the seal settles there easily. Then we jump in the car and race for the ferry.

We arrive at the small airport in plenty of time. I carry the seal now, its face pressed against my neck. The airline personnel and the passengers in the waiting room gaze at the seal with amazement. Everyone wants to stroke its smooth fur. And it gazes back at them with large tender eyes.

When the small plane arrives I ask the pilot if we can fly with the seal. He checks his passenger list and tells us there is room. The airline attendants inform us the flight will be free. And a few minutes later we are strapped in our seats on the plane. Tom is on a seat in front of me with the seal in his lap. I feel its absence like an ache. But Tom seems happy holding it, this seal which is not mine and never will be mine. We fly low over the green islands that float in a deep blue sea. An hour later we make a gentle descent.

Jessica is there waiting at the small airport. She greets us smilingly and takes us in her car to the animal shelter. As soon as we get there she and two other young women attend to the seal. They take its temperature. It is one hundred, which is normal for a seal. They give it a shot of antibiotics and listen to its lungs. Then they weigh it. It weighs sixteen pounds. A seal weighs about twenty pounds when it is born, so this one is badly in need of nourishment. And then they feed it by inserting a tube into its stomach. The seal's protests are mild. In a few moments it is full and sleepy. They place it in an enclosure where it turns on its side and sleeps.

Jessica is grateful that we took care of the seal. The milk and fish may have saved its life she feels. It is in much better shape than she expected. There are no signs of pneumonia. It is weak and dehydrated but it should be fine. She will keep it for about three months. It will weigh sixty pounds when it is released. She shows us photographs of seals they have released. Those large rounded creatures bear little resemblance to the infant seal.

Then she answers my many questions. She tells us mother seals never leave their babies for more than four to six hours. A lot of misinformation on the subject abounds. And seals do not have to be wet. In fact when they are so dehydrated and thin they have no layers of fat to protect them from the cold. In a few days when the seal is stronger, she will place it in a large enclosure with a pond and a ramp. And another young seal will be arriving that will be placed there too. The seals will enjoy each other's company. But when they are released they will each go off alone.

The clinic is in an old house. There are animals and birds inside and out. A great horned owl blinking slowly and a red winged hawk. An albino deer with misshapen legs who wouldn't be able to survive in the wild. Two ferocious baby raccoons who get bottle fed. One of the women puts on thick leather gloves before she lifts one. It growls and claws the air fiercely until it realizes there is milk in its mouth. The moment the bottle is empty it begins to snarl again and flail wildly with its paws. The livingroom has been given over to a full-grown raccoon with paralyzed back legs. The rug is strewn with cereal and toys. The raccoon drags itself contentedly around the room, approaching us for handouts and for strokes. Tom and I stroll around and look at the animals. We say goodbye to Jessica. And take a last and lingering look at the seal who is sleeping deeply and peacefully.

Then we stroll back to the airport along the island roads. The day is warm and green fields stretch out around us. At the airport the desk clerks bring us coffee and ask for news of the seal. A cat that lives here climbs up on a sunny windowsill to sleep. Soon our plane is ready to leave. Everyone thanks us and waves goodbye. We board a small plane that climbs back into the sky. The surface of the blue sea is motionless. And far below I can see the currents that flow like rivers beneath the sea. We fly over many islands and finally over the island where I have lived for seven years. Below me I can see my cabin and the beach lit by the late afternoon sunlight.

In the evening Jannik comes to the cabin for news of the seal. Kerosene lanterns glow and outside the open window the sea brushes into shore. The world is reduced to simple elements, to wind and earth and sea and flame. We sip tea that I prepare on the woodstove and I quietly tell him about the day that was a rare gift and about the seal who is warm now and full and safe. We talk for awhile and then we say goodbye. Jannik has just arrived on the island and I am ready now to depart.

There is something we long for, mother, and all of the days and the nights are not enough. I can still feel the shape of a seal in my arms and the warm soft mouth searching mine. It is early morning. The wind is blowing and the cabin is empty. I leave the door open behind me. A light rain is beginning to fall.

Thursdays

... These are the witnesses:
the Thursdays, and the bones of my arms,
the solitude, and the rain, and the roads ...
—Cesar Vallejo

SEPTEMBER 4

I turn away from the foggy coast and head inland to the camp. It is a minimum security prison about seventeen miles up a winding mountain road. I will be teaching a class there in creative writing. Another instructor who teaches there, Karen, has prepared me somewhat. She has assured me the men are all right. Their crimes are non-violent, mostly connected with drugs. "Be open with them," she tells me. I have wanted to teach at this camp for a long time but tonight as I approach it I wonder why I am here. A logging truck in front of me slows as it climbs a long hill. I am glad of the delay. I find myself hoping he won't pull over to let me by. It is only a few moments later that I come to a sign for the camp and I pull off the road and turn my engine off. I sit there quietly. And then I drive in.

I park by the guard station and enter a building. The guards greet me unsmilingly. They direct me to an adjacent room behind a sliding glass door. Then they announce the class over a loud speaker and the men wander slowly in. We say hello to each other as they enter. A homely gray dog comes in also. I awkwardly move the big tables around the room to form a square. The men just watch me. As I am about to move the last table a man comes and lifts it. "I'll do it," he says quietly and firmly when I try to help.

I hand out some registration forms and big yellow pads of paper along with some already sharpened pencils I have brought with me. I realize everything I planned for tonight is wrong. I sit looking around trying to still my runaway thoughts. The men bend over the registration forms. One man has a face etched with heartache. There is a handsome and solemn older man with a bandanna around his head. There is a man whose smile reminds me of my son. They are both named Jeff. The dog walks around aimlessly. The men seem fond of him but one man suddenly orders him outside. There are three or four men who are Mexican. They struggle with English and I struggle to understand them. An earnest-looking man named Charles tells me Karen asked him to look after me. He has been to college and once took a creative writing class. He suggests that I pass around a piece of paper for an attendance list and I quickly agree. I cannot seem to think. Or maybe I am thinking so many thoughts at once that I cannot grab hold of a single one.

As I gaze around the room I realize these men would like to make friends with me. "Don't be afraid," one of them tells me. "Okay," I answer, and then manage a smile for them. "I've heard you are good guys." They smile back. None of them have written much before except for letters. And these are their only link to their girlfriends or wives or children. They worry that their letters are dull or that they cannot find the right words. We talk about letter writing. And we talk about journals and poetry and fiction and about the kind of center writing might give to their days. They listen and nod. They seem to already know.

Then I ask them to write an introduction to themselves. Charles says he has to visit the restroom and leaves. And the others begin to write. The classroom windows are open and the air is warm. I listen to the crickets droning in the darkness that has swept down like a cloak. There is nothing for miles around but meadows and deep forests.

When the men are finished writing they read their pieces aloud. A man named Robert is an addict and writes about heroin. He talks about how he loves it. He laughs as he reads about his attempted robbery and how badly he bungled it. He was caught on the roof before he even got inside. Frank writes about holes. It is a funny piece about how we are born from a hole and we see and smell and hear and eat from holes and when we die we go back into a hole. We all end up laughing and the men break into clapping. As the others read aloud I notice they all insert *blank blank* for curses. In the college classes I have taught the curses are left intact. I wonder if a former instructor has asked them to do that or if their own sensitivity demands it. I am not sure how I feel about it. A Mexican man reads his introduction. He writes about waking at dawn and saying his prayer and then walking outside in the early morning light to watch the deer.

These men have dignity and openness. They write about their hunger for the sights of the world they are shut away from, cars and buses and stores and people. They write of missing their children and they write of anger at the guards. This morning a man was *rolled up*. Robert explains that this means a man is sent away from the camp. He writes about saying goodbye to this man, someone he hardly knew. He tells Robert to take all the classes he can and not to drop out. Robert is moved by the statement, by the caring it shows. The dropout rate during all of the classes is severe. This one begins with sixteen people. I've heard they usually end with five or six. I wonder about Charles who hasn't returned. Later one of the men tells me he is sick.

When the men are finished reading I ask them a few questions about their life at the camp. They tell me they are allowed visitors on the weekends. They must meet with them in this room where we are sitting. They don't seem to mind, for the room provides them with some sense of privacy. And there is a cabin called Fort Bliss where their wives and girlfriends are allowed to stay with them for a few days. They work during the day at brush clearing or road work and help at forest fires when they are needed. At night they are free to do what they want. They talk of chess and reading. I promise to try and bring them some books.

As I close the class I realize they are not quite ready to leave. They want to talk more about the courage it takes to write and the courage it takes to read aloud. And I confess how nervous I was when I came. Then they slowly leave the room. Many of them stop to say thank you or goodnight.

When they are gone I go to the room where the guards are sitting to tell them I am leaving. I ask them if there is anything I should know and they invite me to sit down. They want me to know how coercive the prisoners are. They warn me to refuse any requests or any presents. I am not allowed to mail letters or make phone calls for the men. They believe all requests would be an attempt to use me. I should even refuse the men cigarettes. One of the guards hands me a printed list of regulations.

SEPTEMBER 11

I arrive at camp early. I stop across the road in a clearing and get out of the car. Quail glide across the meadow like skaters. Late afternoon sun pours down. I follow a path to the creek. Birds are flitting through the trees.

When I drive into camp I stop to read the signs posted along the road: "All visitors entering this property are subject to an official search" and "No admittance except on official business." I park at the guard station.

Tonight the atmosphere seems easy and relaxed. Men are standing on the porch and chatting and a new guard greets me with a friendly smile. He tells me most of the men are out fighting a fire. And he shows me into a small room with a long table and a pot of coffee. "It will be better since the group is small tonight," he says.

Only four men show up. One is new. His name is Reuben and he seems quiet and sincere. He has done business writing but never had the chance to try to be more creative. Tom is young and talkative. He tells me his girlfriend has a locker filled with writing, all the poems and stories she has written since she was five years old. Thomas still wears a bandanna tied around his head. He sits next to me and our hands touch for a few seconds as I hand him a pen. I glance away but feel his eyes study me to see if I have noticed. He tells us he is a Cherokee Indian, a holder of the pipe. He seems to have a deep sense of family and belonging. When he leaves here he will probably head for the large family ranch in Oklahoma. "It's only in California that I get busted," he says with an ironic smile. Herbert is a black man who wears dark glasses that hide his eyes. He has been writing poems for a long time. He wants to write a book someday. And he isn't sure he wants to be in a class. Last week his introduction was brief: "Writing means everything to me." He has a deep sense of privacy.

I give the men a pile of books I have brought them. A bookstore in town has agreed to donate books all during the term. It is an odd assortment that I bring. There are a few westerns, a science fiction book and some Shakespearean plays.

I ask them to write down a dream they have had sometime in their life, one that moved them. Afterwards I make copies of their work. There is a copy machine in another room that the guards tell us we can use. Herbert is reluctant to have a copy made of his writing until we agree to give him the copies back afterward. And then we read the dreams aloud. Thomas writes about a recurring nightmare of being back in a jail. Herbert writes of a city across the road from the sea. Tom writes of a beach and the sea and the freedom of a bird. And Reuben writes:

> I find myself walking on a sandy beach. I can hear the waves
> strike against the rocks and see the spray of mist fly into the
> air. The sand captivates my attention. So many particles. I am
> just a particle of sand on earth. The beach is so long. Where
> am I. I'm here but who am I and what does it matter.

I ask them to choose one of the dreams to talk about and to free associate with and finally for each to write a poem. They choose Reuben's dream and we talk about it for awhile. Then they read their poems aloud. We all seem to agree that Reuben's writing of the dream itself was the true poem.

I feel uncertain as a teacher here. I still can't seem to think. These men seem vulnerable and tender hearted. They are aware that their spelling and grammar is poor but that isn't important. There is a composition class they can take to learn those things. They want to express themselves and in response they want a simple and human appreciation. They are nervous and unsure and I am too.

We spend the rest of the evening just talking. And the men seem happy to do that. Now and then the young guard appears in the doorway kidding all of us. When he leaves the room I ask the men if the atmosphere changes enormously according to which guards are on duty. They agree that it does. I feel like I am in a different place tonight. The mood of the men seems lighter as they describe their days here. Thomas is in charge of maintenance. He works only when something is in need of repair. The others also describe light workloads. They earn a dollar or two a day. They are free to roam the area. And they have dammed the creek to make a swimming hole.

I tell them that I am writing a story about a woman who is teaching a class at a prison camp. They seem pleased but do not question me about it. They want me to bring a story I told them about last week when they asked what I wrote. It is a story of a baby seal and I agree to bring it. But I am not sure. There is love and longing in the story. It reveals a lot about me as a woman. Maybe I will bring it later in the term.

Tom tells a long story about being released from prison after serving a year. He and a friend, he tells us, were both found guilty of a crime they didn't do. He is driven to the bus station wearing a funny pin-striped suit. Along the way he meets another man dressed in the same way. It's a long rambling tale of friendship and roaming around. Somewhere along the way he is arrested again for having a loaded gun in his glove compartment. I encourage him to write the story, and I talk to Thomas about writing about his tribe and his life.

And then class is over. We seem to say goodnight many times. And finally we spill out into the darkness and part.

SEPTEMBER 18

Two spotted fawns run across the road as I drive into camp. A light rain is falling.

I feel confused tonight as the men walk in. There are two new students. And though that first night I had the feeling I would never forget their faces, many of the men look unfamiliar. There is a long awkward pause as the two new men register for class. I look around and slowly begin to remember a few of the faces. I tell Jeff that my son has the same name. He gives me a sweet smile in response. Herbert and Charles aren't here tonight. And I have a feeling they will not be back. And Thomas with his Cherokee blood and his quiet assurance is absent. There was a quiet current of feeling between us. I wonder if that has caused him to step away.

I distribute some New Yorker magazines a friend has given me. And I have brought some books to read passages from. I read a selection from *The Dharma Bums* by Kerouac where the narrator is huddled in fear near the top of a mountain. He watches his friend Japhy run and leap down. Soon he runs and leaps after him, shouting in joy his new discovery that you can't fall off a mountain. And I read a passage by Edward Abbey describing his first night in a trailer at Arches National Monument where he has taken a job for the Park Service. As I read I look up and meet the eyes of the men. They listen with a hushed attention. I wonder when the last time was that someone read aloud to them.

Tom has brought in a love poem he wrote to his girlfriend. And Robert brings a poem about the beauty of the country. There is sensitivity to the writing and the men like the poems. Then on an impulse I ask them to write a journal entry for today. They write for fifteen or twenty minutes. And then we spend the rest of the evening reading their entries aloud and discussing them. Don writes about holding his newborn baby and watching it sleep in his arms. Sod, a new member, writes a funny piece about his friend Cash Register, companion on many youthful escapades. To his amazement he sees his picture years later on a billboard. He is running for political office. Tom writes openly about problems with his girlfriend. There is sadness in his smile tonight.

They write of life at the camp, of the early risings and the quiet companionship they find at breakfast. They write of idle hours and of longing. And they write of the evenings when the deer gather on the lawn. One of the journal entries is about what it is like for members of a highway work crew. It describes the stares and the fear and the anger of those who drive by. All of the men have had that experience and find the rejection painful. I have seen the work crews from time to time through the years, seen the unsmiling men staring with hunger at each passing car. And many years ago I first saw men from the camp at a brush fire. I was on the crest of a hill watching the fire fighters. They stopped what they were doing and gazed up at me. I stood there spellbound, bewildered and compelled by the longing in their faces. A friend quietly explained that they were prisoners and led me away.

The men go on talking for awhile about their experiences in public. I suggest to them that the fear they encounter may be fear the others have of themselves, of their own dark side. The sight of the prisoners strips away for a moment their own sense of safety. They describe a young man who once drove by crossing his wrists before him as if they were handcuffed together. The gesture could have symbolized brotherhood or a cruel mockery.

There is a feeling of a group that is working together tonight. It has taken three weeks for that feeling to begin to emerge. The men talk about how much better the writing is tonight. We all have the feeling that the class has just begun. And somewhere during the evening my own armor seems to have dissolved.

I ask them what the fire was like last week. After a long ride they arrived to find that it had already been contained. They are given steaks for dinner, the best meal they have had in a long time. We go on talking about journals and they promise to continue to write entries during the week. And then we say goodnight.

Tom stays behind for a few moments to talk as the others leave. He tells me about his girlfriend. She is in detention now and her father has had a stroke. He is hoping she will be able to visit. His first request was turned down, but the lieutenant has promised to try to arrange it. His face looks young and eager and sad. If it weren't for the guards outside the door, I would hug him before I leave. But instead I say a gentle goodnight.

SEPTEMBER 25

I arrive and park across from the camp. Ravens are calling hoarsely from the trees. I climb down to the creek. It is higher now from the rains during the week.

The guards greet me in a business-like way. In the classroom a man is wrapping a clock made from a redwood burl. He has made it and shows it to me. He is sending it to his mother. I give out some manilla folders the men have requested and some more New Yorker magazines. I ask them if they are enjoying them. Reuben tells me he couldn't stop looking at the ads. I laugh with him. Here in this deep green forest we are a long way from the world of glamour and sophistication that the ads portray.

Thomas is back tonight and Tom pokes his head in to tell me he won't be at class tonight. Later I regret not asking him if he is all right. There is a new man named Kurt. He says he was working during the previous classes. And he brings a few poems he has written and reads them to the group. One is a tender love poem addressed to a woman who is having difficulties. And the other is about time spent in Folsom Prison where he was sent by mistake. It is a passionate poem about self-preservation and the wearing of a mask.

Jeff has brought an essay about the animal life at the different camps where he has lived. He writes of bears and a three-legged cat whose hunting abilities were unimpaired and of the masked raccoons that came around for handouts. And I learn from his essay that there are thirty cats here. He calls them the hill cats and the creek cats. There are also three dogs.

Robert brings a stunningly honest story about being sick and out of heroin and a journey to Mexico to buy some when a friend turns up with some money. I am moved by the story and so are the men:

> . . . There's an elation a dope fiend gets when he's sick and that sure fix looms just down the road. The talk becomes animated and you somehow find that elusive energy you need to get you to certain relief.

> I remember crossing the border to Mexico and cruising through the streets of Tijuana. We'd drive through poverty and filth and debris. The air conditioner would be on high with music reverberating off the closed windows. Mexican people loitered or walked on the streets, with another world driving by that they knew nothing about.

I want to talk to the lieutenant about the possibility of publishing some of the writing the men are doing in a local publication. I have talked to him about bringing in books and magazines and he seems interested in the class. He tells me about a professor who was so strict that all of the students dropped the class, except for one. That one stayed out of pity. I ask the men how they like the lieutenant and they respond with warmth. Reuben tells me he is helping him to set up a smokehouse at the camp.

I talk to them about the thoughts I've had about class during the week. I would like to concentrate on journal writing for a month or so and then move on to short stories and to poetry. They seem to like the idea. But several of them still seem confused about what journal writing is. I remind them of what they wrote last week and the many ways it is possible to write in a journal. But the sense of unity and a real beginning that we had last week is gone.

As a way of illustrating the freedom of journal writing, I suggest that everyone write a list of happy moments in their lives. A quiet older man excuses himself. He tells me he would like to come back now and then and listen to the class. But he cannot write. The others write for awhile. When I ask them to read their lists aloud, Jeff is reluctant to go first. And Richard too wants to wait until others have read. As the lists are read I realize how deeply personal they are. And I am saddened by how much beauty they are shut away from . . . the love of their children and their families, mountain climbing and travel and bicycle competitions. The lists reveal the men as adventurers who are filled with a love of life. Kurt, the new man, talks of surfing the big waves in Hawaii and about his love of excitement and danger. The last item on his list is the moment when he learned he is free wherever he is, even in the camp.

Sod includes learning to walk on his list but when I question him, he laughs and says he doesn't really remember. He just put it there. And all the men begin to talk about their rebelliousness, their love of risk and danger. They are aware that this is what has gotten them into trouble. Many of them express a desire for their lives to be different when they are released.

As the men read their lists they often break into conversation with each other. It is masculine understanding and acceptance that they seek, and for awhile my presence seems unimportant. They talk about the difficulty of writing about their private lives in this place where they all live together and have meals together. They have written about crying and love and longing. And they have written openly about fear. And now they talk about the fear of this intimacy. Jeff wants to write fiction and so does Reuben. Greg describes his shyness, his need to get his toes wet a little at a time. I suggest they leaf through a book or magazine and find a sentence that compels them. Then they can try to write a story that begins with that sentence.

I leave wondering if their fragile friendships will deepen or if they will need to retreat into privacy. And I leave wondering if I am sensitive enough or if I am somehow failing them. I hope they will remain in the class. I feel like we are back at the very beginning. I wonder what will happen next.

OCTOBER 2

I sit in the clearing across from camp and watch the fading sunlight. In only a few more weeks it will begin to be dark when I arrive.

The men take a long time to arrive after the guard announces the class. The atmosphere is relaxed. The guard jokes with the men as they enter. Only seven men are present. Richard says he has talked to a few of the students who say class is too hard for them. Greg and Sod will be back, but they can't come tonight.

Tom is back and I ask him if he has gotten permission for his girlfriend to visit. He says yes. But he is quiet and again I find myself wondering if he is all right. The dog wanders in. The men tell me his name is Skillet. Jeff is there with his dictionary. He brings it to class each week and as he writes he looks up the spelling of each word he is unsure of. I tell him about a thesaurus and several of the men seem intrigued. It turns out that there is one in the camp and someone goes to get it.

A few men have brought in some writing. Jeff has written a fantasy about a pig race at the camp. It is a funny imaginative piece and the men like it. Tom brings the opening of his long rambling story. The narrator picks up his brother and then announces to him that they are not going home:

> . . . he says where are we going to go I say I don't know let's
> go to Tennessee and find a southern belle and bring her
> back to California or start a new life there . . .

There is no punctuation but there is an easy rhythm to the prose. We all encourage him to go on with it. Robert brings a gentle and mysterious love poem. When I suggest to him that a title would make it clearer, he names it "A Woman Named Nelson." And he goes on to explain that Nelson was the name of an old black woman, a prison guard on the gun rail when he was in the hold in San Quentin. He was moved at hearing the voice of a woman after a long time of only being with men. He wanted to show her the poem but was afraid that she would misunderstand. Though he wrote the poem years ago, he had been thinking of it lately. He asked his wife to look through a large folder of his writings and send it to him.

We begin talking about poetry and read a few of the poems I have given out. One is a poem by Cesar Vallejo entitled "To My Brother Miguel." There is a very quiet Mexican man in the class named Miguel and he smiles shyly at hearing his name in the poem. He asks if I could bring the poem in Spanish. The others also want to hear it in Spanish. I'm left wondering why I haven't thought of this. The Spanish speaking men will like reading the South American poets aloud in their own melodic language. And it will enrich the poems for all of us.

Next we read some haiku. Jeff is eager to understand what a poem is and how it is written. I have chosen poems without rhyme, and he and Reuben have always believed a poem has to rhyme. Tom listens quietly. He and his girlfriend both rhyme all their poems and I wonder what he is thinking.

The guard has been wandering in and out of the room all evening. Now and then he mocks us all. And he announces several times that he is going to attend class next week. He has been out of the room for awhile. Suddenly the glass door slides open loudly and we all look up. The guard stands with a gun pointed at all of us. There is a long silent moment when no one moves. And then the guard is laughing and showing us a toy pistol. One of the men in the camp had just pointed it at him. He tells us he has faced guns several times and has quietly accepted the fact that he will die. "But if they miss, it is a different story," he laughs. Jeff makes a funny grimace at me and I make one back. And finally the guard wanders out. "Pretty lax around here tonight," Jeff says, and the others agree. "You should put that in your story," Tom tells me, and I tell him that I will.

As the room settles down again we read a few more haiku. Then I ask everyone to try writing one. When they are ready Tom collects them and makes copies for all of us on the copy machine in the next room. And we read them aloud. Frank's poems seem to be everyone's favorite:

> It looks like it's dark
> Through the many trees the sun still shines
> It is morning or evening

We suggest changing it to:

> It looks like it's dark
> Through the trees the sun is shining
> Is it morning or evening

The syllables still aren't right. There should be five in the first line, seven in the second and five in the third. But we are satisfied.

And Frank has written another haiku:

> So many days begin today
> Neither to look back or look ahead
> What about right now

Together we revise it:

> Many days begin today
> Don't look back or look ahead
> What about right now

Frank's brow is always furrowed as if he is thinking deeply. He doesn't seem to hear our praise. I tease him gently, asking if he can repeat what we have said. And finally he does and breaks into a smile.

Jeff asks me to bring in more books to read aloud to them. And Tom asks again about the seal story. I promise to bring it in at the end of the term. Class seems to have sped by tonight and we say goodnight.

As I leave I see Sod and tell him we missed him in class tonight. The guard is there and gives a hopeless shrug at my words and says an abrupt goodnight. There seems to be subtle backlash here. I can feel it and almost name it. I have gotten closer to the men tonight. I've found myself being playful and affectionate with them.

I am beginning to trust these men on a deeper level as the weeks go by. Perhaps teaching is always a slow unfolding of love. But this is a prison camp. The guard with his toy pistol and his curt goodnight is a reminder of who is in charge here. I must be careful for my own sake and for the men.

OCTOBER 9

Tonight the guard station is locked when I arrive. I stand on the porch and watch men walking around the camp. No one looks familiar. Someone calls to me from across the road that a guard will be there in about five minutes. And for a moment I feel vulnerable standing there alone on the porch.

The guard arrives to let me in. It is the same guard that was here last week. But tonight there is no joking around and no further mention of attending the class. I go to the copy machine to duplicate some poems I have brought. Tom and Jeff come in to make some copies too. Tom seems happier tonight. The dean of my college arrives. He is here to observe my teaching. I introduce him to the men and for the next hour we all remain aware of his silent presence there.

I have brought a box of books and the men look through them. Don takes a book on child raising. He has spent last weekend with his wife and new baby. He tells me it was a good visit. A man named Patrick registers for the class. He has just arrived at the camp. He likes to write songs and poems and is pleased that there is a creative writing class.

After a long time of giving out papers and books and waiting for Patrick to register we settle down to work. Jeff has brought a few short prose pieces. And Reuben, who has been questioning me seriously about poetry, brings in a whole page of haiku:

> White clouds in the sky
> Shadows searching far below
> I cannot hide

> The hills talk of time
> Animals roam and grass grows
> Why do they whisper

Everyone is pleased by the haiku. And Don begins a story about a friend and a boat and growing marijuana. He also hands me a few pages of journal entries that he doesn't feel comfortable reading in class. Robert hasn't brought anything tonight. He says he just hasn't been in the mood to write.

We talk for a few moments about the importance of the mood for writing. I mention that taking a long walk sometimes helps one to get in the right state of mind. A few of the men mumble that they can't take a long walk here. It was Thomas who had given me the feeling the men could walk wherever they wanted. I was surprised but I believed him. I do not question the men. It is the first time they have seemed ashamed.

Thomas hasn't been to class in weeks. And the older man who said he couldn't write has not returned. Herbert also is gone, the man who cared too much about writing to submit his work to the group. There are others too that have quietly disappeared. There are eight people in class tonight. I hope they will stay.

I have brought in some more Spanish poems tonight and I ask a few of the men to read the poems aloud in English. And then Reuben and Robert read them aloud in Spanish. I had hoped Miguel and Frank would be here but they are both absent tonight. We save the poem bearing Miguel's name for him to read aloud next week. There are a few gentle and fanciful poems by Garcia Lorca. The men seem puzzled and also drawn to the poems. And I wonder if perhaps for a moment they feel their own gentleness authenticated by the poems.

And then I do a fiction exercise with the men. It is one I had hoped to use several weeks ago, I tell them laughingly. This class seems to find its own direction and I just follow along. But now I ask the men to think of a character and to write down the character's name. And then I begin asking them questions about their character. The dean gets up quietly and thanks me, patting my shoulder as he leaves. Tom says to me with a twinkle in his eye, "That's like having a guard in the room. But this time it is your guard." I smile and nod.

For the next hour or so the men write answers to my questions. *Where does your character live? What does he look like? What is his relationship like with a wife or a girlfriend or a friend? What change is happening in his life?* When I run out of questions, they add some more.

We take a break to stretch and get coffee and then they read the answers aloud. They have chosen a wide variety of characters. One is an inmate at Soledad prison and one is a married man troubled by his daughter who has to be institutionalized. And Patrick, the new student, writes of a prince living in fifteenth century England. His kingdom has been stolen and now he is a renegade who roams the countryside.

There isn't time to begin the stories tonight and so we talk for awhile before departing. The men begin describing a new cat who has turned up at the camp. They say it is full of personality, visiting their rooms unexpectedly and sleeping on their clothes. Most of the cats here are wild, but this one seems fond of human company. They seem impressed by its tree climbing skills. I start to ask them a question but I realize I would be interrupting. They are talking to one another. There is an eagerness, a hopefulness in the air. It leaves me wondering.

We all walk outside finally into a foggy night and say goodnight. I drive home slowly hardly able to find the road in the deep white mist. And at home at last before the fire, I read the journal pages Don has given me. He writes about the negativity of the camp and a fear of spending a long time in that dark atmosphere. And he writes of a few isolated conversations he has had with other men. I read the final paragraph:

> Thursday night's class is the first place I've seen a group
> of people begin to let down some of the barriers, the same
> barriers one learns to keep up in order not to be victimized.
> Not everyone preys on one's weaknesses but you don't
> know who does. This class is the first place I've been which
> feels like a safe place.

OCTOBER 16

There is a fine rain falling as I drive into camp. The guard station is locked again and I stand in the deepening twilight watching the men slowly leaving the dining hall. A few of them stop on the lawn to feed four cats that are gathered there.

Jeff and Tom and Reuben appear and wait with me on the porch. And a group of men I don't know are also waiting. The guard finally comes, the same guard who has been here for the last few weeks. "What a bunch of losers," he says to the men. "I'm not a loser. I'm a winner," one of them replies. "Some winner," the guard answers as he unlocks the door.

I have a letter with me for the lieutenant but I find I am reluctant to leave it with this guard. I decide to wait until next week. It contains a list of books I am hoping he will consider purchasing for the camp. I have talked to him on the telephone and he is interested in starting a small library for the men. I ask him about the possibility of publishing some of the class writing. "No, I wouldn't permit that," he says. He goes on to tell me that many of the men are illiterate. The guards who screen their letters to their girlfriends are often amused for they copy poems from books and claim to have written them. I learned several weeks ago that a creative writing class will not be offered at the camp next term. The lieutenant informs me that he wants to have a remedial English class at the camp. And before we hang up he tells me he is looking forward sometime to meeting me.

Tom and Jeff collect the writing from the group and go to copy it for us. Patrick appears with a long story he has begun. But he didn't go to work today because he was ill and isn't sure if he will be allowed to attend class tonight. He goes to inquire and comes back to tell us sadly that he will bring his story next week.

Robert begins the class with a poem he has just written. The men respond warmly but Robert doesn't like the poem. He is still having trouble writing. I suggest that he sit by the creek to write but the men explain that once the swimming hole is closed they are not permitted at the creek. Then they talk for a few moments with resignation about how many of the rules seem arbitrary here.

Jeff continues with his theme of animals. He has begun a story about raising pedigreed cats. He tells us he used to have horses as well as dogs and a number of kittens that he raised on a bottle. And he reads us a short and moving poem about a dog that lives at the camp:

Knuckles

Old dog, old dog, come and lay your
old head on my knee
Dear God, dear God, let this poor
creature go and live in peace.

And Reuben has written two new haiku:

Trees soundly sleeping
Waking stars taking a stroll
Crickets are chirping

Fearful of first flight
They nest together in fright
Now they soar the sky

He asks if I can bring in more haiku and I tell him that I will.

Tom hasn't written anything this week but he brings a poem his girlfriend has copied for him from a poetry book. He doesn't know who wrote it but is eager to find out. It is a long poem entitled "A Woman's Question," and in it a woman is seeking to define a love that will endure. And Don reads a few more pages of his story about a boating trip.

Miguel is here tonight and reads us some new Spanish poems I have brought in, and also the Vallejo poem with his name. From his reading we can sense a long familiarity with poetry. I have also brought Vallejo's "Black Stone on a White Stone." After Miguel has read it aloud in Spanish, I read it in English. I wonder what the men are feeling as I read:

> . . . never so much as today have I
> found myself
> with all the road ahead of me, alone.

There is still some time left in class but I am uncertain suddenly about what we should do. There has been a strange mood of despondency in the air all evening and the words of the poem still seem to echo. Don asks if they can do more exercises and for a few moments I try to think of one. I ask if they would like to write another list and they agree. And then I ask them to write a list of things they want to do in life that they have never done before.

Miguel has been writing down eagerly a long poem he memorized years ago. As soon as he is done he reads it aloud to us. He is so engrossed in the poem he doesn't even notice that he is interrupting the men. Some of them go on writing and the Spanish seems to flow like music in the background. And then he translates into his broken but sensitive English. The poem is about a widower who drinks each evening until he can see and talk to his dead wife. His young son, filled with longing to see his mother, picks up the bottle one day and drinks. When the bereft man realizes what has happened, he never drinks again. Miguel asks me excitedly if I can bring in some Mexican and Cuban poetry. But since I live in a small and remote town, I doubt if I will be able to find any.

The men have finished their lists and the mood begins to lift a little as they read:

> Go in a space shuttle and view the earth
>   from high above
> Sing in front of others
> Fly a helicopter
> Be a good human being
> Help the young and handicapped
> Travel to Bali
> Direct and control my own destiny

As I listen I find myself wishing we were somewhere else. I picture us in a café or in my living room before a warm fire. There are questions I would like to ask the men and thoughts I would like to share with them but the guards behind the glass doors prevent me.

Reuben and Miguel stay behind after the others leave. Miguel is worried about his poor English. He is considering dropping out of class. Reuben and I try hard to dissuade him and I think we succeed. And then I talk to Reuben about sending some haiku to a poetry magazine. He likes the idea.

I drive home along the quiet winding roads. The moon is almost full. The night is brushed with shadow and with light.

OCTOBER 23

I sit in my car in the clearing across from camp. It is raining and white mist drifts slowly over the trees. I browse through a poetry book and find a poem by Galway Kinnell that I want to read to the men:

> . . . I know that I love the day,
> The sun on the mountain, the Pacific
> Shiny and accomplishing itself in breakers
> But I know I live half alive in the world,
> I know half my life belongs to the wild darkness.

The guardhouse is locked again and I wait on the porch with Jeff and Tom. We watch the cats. Jeff explains that there are two separate territories for the hill cats and the creek cats. Between them is a line that cannot be crossed. A black and white cat stands looking hopefully toward the lawn where other cats are eating scraps. It takes a step or two forward and then retreats.

The men have brought a lot of writing tonight, and Jeff and Tom and Reuben take charge of copying it and collating and stapling. It takes a long time and the rest of us wait. I leave the book list for the lieutenant with a new guard, and then wander back into the room. Greg is here tonight. He has only come a few times. He explains that he isn't writing anything and that makes him reluctant to attend. But he has brought some writing from a friend in prison.

Robert has brought a story. He is hard to know with his warm ironic smile and low gruff voice. But I have come to like him and respect his sensitivity. Patrick has returned with his story. When he first appeared two weeks ago, he boasted happily about his wild imagination. But now he is nervous and explains apologetically that his spelling and grammar are poor and he doesn't really know anything about writing.

When the papers are finally assembled we begin. I read aloud the Galway Kinnell poem and the group seems to like it as much as I do. I have brought in some haiku by Basho in response to the request from Reuben. I also bring him the address of a magazine where he can submit some of his haiku. Tonight Reuben has written the start of a story. He has never written a story before and there is a lot of caution in the writing. We talk about the importance of getting closer to the character and he seems to understand.

Tom turns in a poem which is a prayer:

> . . . so lord I trust you
> The future is all thine
> Just help me to live
> One day at a time

The poem is written so smoothly that for a moment I wonder if he wrote it. It takes courage here for the men to allow their vulnerability to show. It seems almost the same impulse to write a poem as to claim one. Someone suggests titling it "Jail House Blues" and Tom agrees. He had wanted the word jail in the title. He tells us he has written a number of poems about God, and I encourage him to bring them.

Jeff brings a few more pages from his story about cats. We encourage him to add many more details to the story. I feel freer tonight to make suggestions about the writing. The men seem to be beginning to trust themselves as writers and also to trust that their writing will be treated with respect.

Patrick reads his fantasy. It has grammatical errors, as he feared, but there are some lovely lyrical passages:

. . . And during his sleep his father spoke to him in a dream telling him that there was power in the locket given to him as a boy . . . His father told him that the stone inside, when facing a full moon, could answer questions and foretell events and give advice but was only to be used by the first born of the bloodline. Awoken by the astonishment of the dream, he quickly examined the locket of gold hanging on his neck given to him on his thirteenth birthday and opened it and examined the stone inside . . .

Greg reads the story his friend has written. It is a funny farcical yarn that is full of charm. The men laugh so loudly that I grow nervous about the guards. The group breaks into applause at the end. And then Greg goes on to talk about his own writing. He used to write frequent letters but he hardly ever writes anymore. Incoming and outgoing mail is read by the guards. And they sometimes make jabbing references to something they have read. So far the writing in class is uncensored. I wonder it if will remain that way.

Robert reads a story about his first car. He loved it dearly, even though it only ran once in all the years he had it:

In the summer the heat waves would shimmer in the air, and the dead cattail weeds would sit up around the tires of my grand Chevrolet. I'd sit with the window open with my left elbow expertly hanging out the window. I'd imagine myself cruising on a cool summer evening. I'd also sit in my car in the rain, and stick my hand up under the dashboard, and work the windshield wipers with my hand . . .

I try to let Robert know how good his writing is and so do the men. We point out all the wonderful details he always includes. Robert listens and smiles his ironic smile. And then he thanks us. But I am not sure that he believes us.

When the class is ending, Don asks me if it will be taught again in the spring. I tell him that it won't, but perhaps will be offered again next fall. "I'll be gone," he says with a smile. "I like the class a lot, but not enough to come back for it." Greg says he will be here. And then he tells me he has three more years to serve. And that he has already been here for two years. I had thought the men were here for only one year or two at most. "Writing might help," I tell Greg softly and he agrees.

Class has ended but we linger for awhile. Robert asks when I will read something of my own. I repeat my promise to read my seal story on the last day. Tom asks me about the camp story. "Will you read that too," he asks. I am worried about finding a few pages that will be all right to read to them. I cannot possibly go back on my word. There is a feeling here that I am sometimes aware of. It is hard to name it . . . an innocence perhaps or an eagerness in the faces of the men, an unspoken plea that I treat them fairly. It makes me humble. I hope I am gentle enough. I hesitate for a moment and then I assure Tom that I will. We say goodnight and step out together into the darkness. And then I drive home slowly through the deep fog that has settled everywhere.

OCTOBER 30

Tonight it is dark when I arrive. I sit for awhile listening to the rushing of the creek. I have brought a book of my poems with me. The men have asked so often to hear something I have written. It doesn't seem right to make them wait until the last class.

When we are all gathered, I read them a group of poems. They listen intently but afterwards they have little to say. I feel awkward asking them how they like the poems. Instead we talk about writing and publishing. The book was published by a small press and they are surprised that I wasn't paid for the writing. They are under the impression that writers make a great deal of money. They ask me to pass the book around and I do. Greg reads it carefully and says he wishes he could keep it longer. I tell him he can have it for the week. He notices how often islands appear in the poems. He has always wanted to own his own island and I have also. "This camp is an island," he says, and I know what he means.

Then Robert takes the book. For a long time he pays no attention to what is going on in the class. And I remain aware of him silently reading from cover to cover. He makes no comment when he is done.

Tonight Greg has brought in a bound book with blank pages. His family sent it to him. He reads us his first journal entry. He has written about the events of the day. Then he talks to us about how nervous it makes him to write. Even talking about it, he says, makes his palms sweat. "It must mean a lot to you," I say. He quickly drops the subject.

All during the term the men have teased Jeff about his love of cookies. He has earned the title of The Cookie Monster. Tonight Robert has brought a story that is openly about Jeff. The tone is teasing and affectionate:

> . . . One night as I lay awake in my bed, I heard Jeff begin
> to mumble in his sleep. As I paid closer attention to what he
> was saying, I began to hear a few words being said between
> grunts and growls. I distinctly heard the word Oreo being
> repeated over and over. Other words I heard were peanut
> butter, chocolate chip, sugar cookies and vanilla wafers . . .

Jeff looks pleased and embarrassed. The others respond with laughter and applause. The men seem to have grown closer. They have been showing each other their writing during the week. Robert refused to let anyone see this story so it would be a surprise tonight.

Tom has brought in another poem. Even though he brings something each week, he still seems nervous and unsure. More and more his poems reveal a deep belief in God, and he seems uncertain how the men will respond to this:

> . . . I was all alone frightened
> in a horrid world, soon to be walls of stone
> all alone with no one, no one but hope
> and with only a fix that would help me cope . . .

The poem ends with the realization that only God can help him. The response from the group is a quiet one. But a few of the men say the poem is a good one. I talk to him about line endings and make a few suggestions for changes. And we talk about titles. He feels that all his jail poems belong together under one title and I agree.

Don has finished his story about the boat. Drunk and stoned, the two friends in the story drive home. They painstakingly back the trailer into the drive while the neighbors watch. Then they discover they have lost both the boat and the trailer somewhere along the way. They retrace their ride and find them sitting in the road. We encourage him to work more on the story and fill it in with details and dialogue between the men.

Jeff brings in a poem called "The Time Clock":

This is a place built for time.
People punch in after doing a crime.

It doesn't need winding and you
wont hear any ticks . . .

Some call it jail but I am here to tell.
It is known to all man as the time clock of hell . . .

All of us are moved by the poem.

We have finished with the writing that the men have brought, and we drift off into talk. There was a rainbow over the camp today. And when we walk outside, the night is filled with stars.

NOVEMBER 6

I wait in the darkness for the guard to appear and then go in. The men arrive slowly. I look for Patrick, who was absent last week, but he doesn't come. When I ask Jeff about him, he looks away and says he doesn't know. I get the feeling he won't return. Seven men are attending the class now. I have heard some of the other classes are even smaller.

The men haven't brought much writing tonight. Miguel says he has been writing a poem in Spanish and will try to translate it for us soon. But he is having trouble with words that don't seem to exist in English. The poem is about being a child and watching his mother cook tortillas over the fire. He eats as he watches. When breakfast is finally served, his father wonders why he isn't hungry. His mother keeps silent. The word he is searching for describes the tortillas when they are ready, when they are like a blossom about to open. Usually Miguel is quiet in class but once he begins to talk he is excited and eager. His warm smile transforms his usually solemn face.

Reuben has continued his story. It is about two brothers taking a journey on a train. He reads a new page he has written. He is enjoying the freedom that fiction allows him and promises to write more for next week. Tom has written another poem about prison and about faith in God. This one is entitled "Doing Time With God." A few of the men comment by saying they like the poem. But he isn't satisfied. He wants to hear from everyone. He questions each person and they make a few suggestions and also praise him.

Greg turns in another journal entry. He says he wrote it right after class last week. In it he has recorded his haiku and another one he wrote. I suggest that next he might want to try writing a memory or record a dream. "You wouldn't want me to tell you my dreams," he says teasingly.

Greg has also brought a letter he got today from his friend whose stories and poems he has read in class before. This man seems like an invisible presence here. In the letter he describes a trailer he has rented in the wilderness. He has recently been released from prison and is salmon fishing in the river each day while an eagle fishes nearby. The letter is filled with affection for Greg, whom he has nicknamed Black Sheep.

The men ask me about an exercise I mentioned a few weeks ago. First I describe a scene for them. "You are in New York," I tell them, "and it is nearly Christmas. The weather is very cold and snow is falling. A nineteen year old boy named Joey is standing on the roof of a tall building and threatening to jump." And then I assign each man a character: Joey, Joey's father, a priest, a policeman, Joey's girlfriend, a taxi driver, and a prostitute. I ask them to write the thoughts or stream of consciousness of their character. They seem captivated by their assignments and begin to write. After a little while, Tom and Miguel dramatically fling their pencils down. And a few moments later everyone is done. We make copies and read them aloud.

Jeff takes the part of Joey and the piece he writes is moving:

> I am afraid. I am nervous. It's cold. I'm cold. What am I going to do? Why am I up here. God help me. What am I going to do . . . I don't know if I want to jump now. How did I get myself in this mess. If I don't jump, I probably will go to jail or something or a mental place. What am I going to do . . .

I have done this exercise a number of times with other classes, but none of us have ever thought about the trouble Joey will be in if he quietly changes his mind.

Tom writes touchingly as Joey's father:

> I've tried to raise him right with love . . . I've tried and his mother has tried to talk with the boy. He won't tell us what is bothering him. All he says is let me be. I will do what I want to do . . . What have we done wrong to you . . .

Miguel's piece as the priest is brief but appropriate:

> . . . Are his parents around. I want to see them and talk to them. Father please change this boy's mind and don't let him jump.

Reuben is the cop. I notice that tonight the men have lifted their own restriction on cursing. And I find I am glad. Don is the taxi driver and Robert is the prostitute. The language they use seems true to character. I think they sense this and sprinkle their paragraphs liberally.

Greg is Joey's girlfriend and his description of their first meeting provides substance to the whole scene:

> Joey, please don't jump . . . How long has it been. I guess
> about two years since we found each other, near the park.
> Joey caught my dog for me after the leash had broken. What
> can I say to keep him from jumping . . .

The men like the anonymity of expressing the feelings of a character so different from themselves. And they like being a small part of a larger scene that is being created. We all agree that they have done a wonderful job.

It is time for class to be over, but again we are all somehow reluctant to leave. They ask again about my story and want to know if there is anything they can tell me about the camp. We talk about slang expressions they use. During each class there are expressions I ask them about that I have never heard before. They think they are probably exclusively prison slang. If someone has *a locker full of cheese,* they tell me, it means that he is a rat or an informer. Two expressions for getting muscular are *getting your jokes* and *getting buffed.* Jeff explains *in the car* and *out of the car* to me. If everyone is having tuna fish sandwiches, you might walk up and ask if you are *in the car.* It means being included. I guess at the meaning of some of the expressions and they laugh. I am almost always wrong.

The men ask me if I will teach at the camp again. I have told them creative writing will not be offered next term, but they are wondering if I could teach something else. They all seem interested in a literature class. The text could be a short story anthology and we could read and discuss a story each week. "We want you to come back," Jeff says. I tell him I want to come back also. I do not tell him that I have already been thinking of the end of class and how much I will miss them. The ending isn't for several months but it seems to already be on all our minds.

I ask them if there is anything special they would like to do during the rest of the term. Robert asks if I will bring in a story to read and talk about. He suggests Steinbeck or Stephen Crane. And I tell him I will. Robert will be released in about two months. I ask him if he will stay out this time, and he laughs his gentle laugh. "Probably not," he says. "The first two days of freedom are higher than any drug but then it wears off," he goes on. "It's okay here, and the food and rent are free." There is a sad irony in his voice. I ask him if he would write a story about a man who gets released from camp and stays out. "A fantasy," he says quietly. "Maybe a rehearsal," I respond. "Sounds like a good idea," he says in a husky tone.

Tom says he will get out in three hundred and sixty four days. His release day is his birthday. He wants to leave California and perhaps go to Kansas. He hasn't mentioned his girlfriend in many weeks. I wonder about that but he seems all right.

As we all slowly drift from the room I am aware suddenly of the guard who is noting our easy familiarity. He stops me as I leave. "The men can no longer make copies," he tells me. "They are not allowed in the copy room. There are things there they are not allowed to have."

The words are cold but there is a touch of kindness in his voice tonight. I tell him the men have been helping me out by doing the copying for the class. He understands that but he cannot allow it any longer. I assure him I will be the only one at the machine from now on. Then we say goodnight.

November 13

Jeff and Reuben and I wait together on the porch. The night is warm and clear. I explain to them that I will have to do the copying from now on. And they tell me stories about the guard. He interrupted last night's class again and again asking when it would end. The instructor kept repeating that she did not know. Finally he entered the room, turned on the television, and sat down to watch it. They also tell me with a smile that the guard will be going on a one month vacation soon.

As we stand in the darkness waiting, a man walks up who will be released tonight. Jeff and Reuben shake hands warmly with him. Then the guard appears and warns him that there are still hours to go so he had better be careful. "That's rude," Jeff tells the guard. He repeats it again. There is a pause in everyone's breathing. The guard does not respond.

Awhile later as I stand at the copy machine, the guard approaches me. "What time will class end?" he inquires. I tell him I am not sure but usually we end at about nine-thirty. And then he tells me that since Reuben is a clerk he will be allowed to do the copying for the class. I feel as if I am in a chess game and have just lost a pawn.

Tonight Jeff brings in a group of haiku. He has been puzzled and frustrated by them since we first began discussing them. And then he reads them to us:

> Yet the bridge remains unchanged
> I saw the far hills change color
> Watched as the city grew

My life is an island
This island in the middle rising up
for this island is my treasure

You must work to maintain
Even a turtle doesn't get ahead unless
he sticks his neck out

I wonder about this gentle man. He has never alluded to what brought him here. He has come to every class bringing his weekly writing. He is proud of his graceful handwriting and every word is spelled correctly. The men seem openly fond of him. We talk about his poems for awhile. He wants to write another animal story but he isn't sure yet what animal to write about.

Robert has brought a journal entry that he hoped would grow into a story. It doesn't really go anywhere but his voice is always compelling:

Let's say I'm going to throw this away, or perhaps burn it, like some dangerous secret when I'm done. Will the writing be different then. I'm always conscious or subconsciously aware of someone else reading what I've written. Does it change or would it change if I could write for myself alone.

Greg is absent tonight. I ask Don if he will deliver a message to him that he just can't quit now. Don laughs and assures me that he'll be coming back. Don hasn't had a chance to write this week. His wife and baby were visiting for four days. And no one else has brought writing. Reuben has been trying to write more haiku but the muse has deserted him. Tom says he is working on his story and will bring it later in the term. Miguel is struggling with English. The words come easily to him in Spanish, but finding the words in English is hard for him. I tell him to bring in some attempts and we will help him.

I give everyone a copy of Hemingway's story "A Clean, Well-Lighted Place" and we read it aloud. The men are moved by the story, by the kindness of the older waiter and the loneliness of the old man. They ask me to bring in more stories. "And poems," Robert adds. And Jeff asks me to bring in love poems. It is a little early and I ask the men if we should end the class. But they are not ready to go.

I decide to try an exercise with them that I am hoping will break through some of their writing blocks. I suggest they write a dialogue between themselves and the writer in them. They can consult the writer about whatever problem they are having and perhaps he will have an answer. The men write for awhile but no one seems to have the energy for it. And finally they are ready to leave.

I gather up my papers, feeling a nameless sorrow. Perhaps Robert feels it also for he lingers for a moment in the doorway. We talk aimlessly and then he leaves. A man is being released tonight and others remain prisoners. Many of them have been in prison a number of times. I am aware of the guard sitting at his desk in the next room and of a feeling of defeat that sometimes enters even this well-lighted room.

> The café is dark now and the old waiter seems to go on chanting:
>
> . . . Our nada who art in nada, nada be thy name thy kingdom nada thy will be nada in nada as it is in nada . . .

NOVEMBER 20

I drive to the camp through rain and fog so thick I can barely find my way. And then I sit in the darkness and listen to the rain falling everywhere.

The men are slow to appear. Miguel isn't here tonight, and for the first time Jeff is absent. A football game is blaring on a television on the other side of the glass doors and the men seem only half present. Their attention drifts again and again to the game.

I have talked to the lieutenant during the week and tell the men about it. He has misplaced the list of books I gave him and is only willing to order a few. I choose a poetry anthology, a collection of short stories and a thesaurus and dictionary. The books have finally been ordered and I am hoping each man will receive a copy of them. They know how slowly things happen around here, but we're all faintly hopeful they will actually appear.

Greg arrives late. Don and Tom have told me he had a rough few days but is better now. He comes in bringing new pages of journal writing to read to us. The passages are honest and moving:

> . . . But what keeps me awake at times is what's up ahead. I think of the bullet that has my name on it. And what I must do to keep from getting it soon. Sometimes I truly wonder who is dead and who is alive but in some ways dying every day . . . I truly have lost most of what I was, in that flash of gun fire.

And then he continues:

> My little play time is over. The game now is harder and I don't know a lot of the rules. Man's worst enemy is truly himself.

And he writes of a new room he has been given. He cherishes the privacy. He has often spoken of his need for solitude, this man who has lived for many years in the mountains far from any town. He tells us that if he returns there, he will be killed. And if he leaves, he will lose his son. No one questions him about this. Instead we talk for awhile about the years he will have to search for an answer to his dilemma. Journal writing is beginning to mean a lot to him and he looks forward to writing more.

Tom talks of his release in a year. "If I don't go to Kansas," he says, "I'm going to build a log cabin on a lake a few hours from here." Don will be free in July. He has a job and wife and baby awaiting him. He seems determined never to return to prison. I don't believe he ever will.

Reuben has just had a three-day family visit and has clerical work to catch up on. He hasn't had any time to write. He helps with the copying but during most of the evening he works next door in an office.

Don has brought in a few poems tonight. One is about the sea:

> Serenity below
> peaks and valleys above
> pass by forever
>
> Each peak reaches high
> to fall on destination
>
> Water to sand
> beach and sea touch
> beginning is end

Tom hasn't written anything for a few weeks. He has left class early several times and tonight too he seems restless and eager to leave. I encourage him to stay for awhile longer. Next week is Thanksgiving and it will be two weeks until we next meet. He promises to have some new poems then.

Robert has a new story. It opens joyfully:

> It was a bright sunshiny Central California day. Everything was right with my whole world. It was that time of year in 1968 when the warmth of summer was beginning to wane and fall was making its presence known with a slight crispness in the air. It was that time in my life where I would sometimes shiver at the sheer joy of being alive. Even though a war in Vietnam was unpopularly being waged somewhere in the world and unrest seemed everywhere, I felt at the eye of the hurricane.

It goes on to describe his being in a crowd of friends when an old derelict approaches them wanting to sell a few packs of cigarettes to get money for wine. They all make mocking comments. Then the old man approaches Robert:

> I said to him, "Here, you take the fifty cents and keep the cigarettes." . . . It was like someone else said it. When I had intended to say something else, my compassion moved me to disregard the group, and give the old man his much needed bottle of wine with two packs to smoke with it. And the feeling I got from it was well worth the fifty cents I paid for it.

Everyone likes the story and the details Robert has used to bring it to life. He tells me he always writes now, right after class. I tell him I hope when he is released he will find another writing class at whatever college is nearby. And he quietly admits how much he is enjoying writing. "And you seem to like what I write," he says with a slow smile, "or else you don't want me to drop the class." I tell him about typing up many of his passages for my story and how fine I think they are. And I think he believes me.

I read the men some poems I have brought in. They listen to the music of "Annabel Lee" with admiration. But mostly their attention drifts to the game. For the first time we end the class early. Though we go on talking for awhile. Tom tells me he has filled in this week for someone. He has been out of camp for several days on long drives to get parts. In a store he had to pay for the parts with a check from the camp. "Are you an inmate there," the young salesgirl asks. She seems to back away from him. But then he goes on eagerly talking about driving along the coast and the beauty of the sea and the taste of freedom.

But Greg goes on thinking of the salesgirl. He says he is ashamed to be here. He doesn't want to learn the prison slang or get on familiar terms with most of the other men. "I don't want anyone to ever be able to tell I have been here," he says.

And then the men tell me that on weekends they are allowed to leave the camp for a walk. They must report in after two hours but then they are allowed to leave for another two hours. It is the best part of their week.

We talk of the creek filling with rain and they say salmon will be spawning there soon. Robert grins and says he has a smokehouse. I tell them about the island where I lived and the salmon we feasted on in the summer and autumn. I ask them to tell me when the salmon begin to spawn. I want to see once again the bruised and weary salmon as they struggle home. Once I looked into a river where salmon were spawning and it was like looking into a dream.

We wish each other a good holiday, but there is sadness in the faces of the men. "Drive safely," Robert says, and we walk out together into the rain.

DECEMBER 4

I drive out to camp through rain and deep fog. Beside me on the seat is a large box of books for the men. The guard station is unlocked and the men arrive more quickly tonight. They break into smiles at the sight of the books. We haven't seen each other for two weeks and the mood is festive. They want to hear about my Thanksgiving and they tell me the guard we all dislike has been transferred to day duty for two months. And they bring a new man with them named David. He has just arrived at the camp and will only be here until February. But he is eager to attend class. He tells me when he gets out he wants to enter a two-year program somewhere in medical technology. His last release only lasted two months and he seems determined to make this next one permanent.

There are not quite enough books for the men. But they divide them easily. With a smile, I give Jeff his thesaurus. They browse through the books and write their names inside. They have brought a lot of writing tonight. Jeff and Tom resume their job of making copies. The guards that are here seem to have no objection. While we are waiting they tell me a few of them have been writing letters for Freddy the cook. He can't write and has been receiving love letters from about four women. So they've been responding for him and it keeps them busy.

Jeff and Tom return with the copies and give them out. And the men ask when classes will end. I explain that there are two more classes and then a Christmas break. And in January there are two last weeks. They ask again about the chance of my teaching here next term and next year. I tell them about something I have been wondering. Perhaps the creative writing class was discontinued next term because I have somehow made myself too visible with the lieutenant. I have called several times and sent him a book list and even asked about the possibility of them publishing. Don assures me that the class is never offered two terms in a row. And they all seem to feel that the decision has nothing to do with me. I trust their knowledge of this place and the way it works. They feel it was probably a decision to offer the men more practical skills.

Jeff has been wearing a woolen hat and Tom teasingly asks him if he is cold. A little while later he quietly takes his hat off. His hair is striped now with shaved lines and I wonder why. He reads first tonight, a new story entitled "Give the Kid the Ball." It describes a ball game in Cincinnati when a foul ball flies into the stands:

> . . . A boy of about nine was reaching for it when the ball was grabbed by a man of about thirty five with horn-rimmed glasses. You could see that the kid was totally crushed. He had on an oversized Cincinnati Reds cap that came over his eyes and a baseball glove that was too big for him. He seemed the kind of kid every other kid on the block beats up daily.
>
> Suddenly someone shouted. Give the kid the ball! The chant was taken up by others around us. Give the kid the ball! Give the kid the ball!

The chant continues until even the ball players are looking up into the stands. And finally the man passes the ball to the boy. The chant changes and grows triumphant. "He gave the kid the ball," the crowd now yells. Two more balls were caught in the stands that day. And the boy goes home with a big grin and three balls in his over-sized glove.

Robert quietly points out that this story is the best that Jeff has written and everyone agrees. Then Robert apologetically presents a poem. He isn't pleased with it and feels he should have written much more during the two weeks:

> . . . Let me with one wave of my
> hand right the terrible wrongs
> of mankind
> Let us know in one eternal
> moment, all knowing
> Let the whole world know right,
> and forever after be right
> So that the garden reappears
> and we become entwined as one
> within . . .

The men comment on the depth and the feeling expressed in the poem.

Tom has turned in a few haiku:

> Birds floating on water
> Skies are clear beauty
> as the water splashes on the rocks

It has been clear for several weeks that Tom and Jeff are confused about syllables. I explain them again, showing them how the mouth moves a little with each new sound. And I show Jeff the way the dictionary divides each word into its syllables. I think I have been gentle enough that they are not embarrassed at their misunderstanding. And the men, who are always sensitive to one another, point out how clear the picture is that Tom's poem paints.

Don turns in a journal entry about a recurrent dream he has. He is with two women and they are in a boat. The boat speeds along the water and suddenly the water is gone. Almost miraculously the boat keeps going over dry creek beds and pavement until suddenly the water surrounds them once again. The dream reminds him of his past and of a high risk lifestyle. "Just like suitcases of money and drugs only different consequences for my actions," he writes.

Reuben has to leave to make a phone call but we talk for a few moments before he goes. His interest has wandered away from class for the last few weeks but tonight he seems ready to write again. I suggest that he try writing down some dreams also. He tells me that when he was a businessman during a hectic troubled period in his life, he used to dream the answer to whatever problems arose. He would wake in the middle of the night amazed to suddenly have a solution. He promises to write something for the next class.

I ask the men about phone calls and they say they are allowed four calls a month. They must sign up on Sundays for any call they want to place during the week. They are allowed to talk for ten minutes and all the calls are taped. Those who have been in other prisons say they were allowed more calls there. The rules seem arbitrary but there is nothing they can do.

I have noticed that Jeff sometimes asks me a question that I have been thinking about and wanted to talk to the men about but wasn't sure how to begin. Tonight he asks me, "How do you feel about us. Are we different from other students and other classes." I tell him that this group seems more open and more sensitive, and he nods his head knowingly. Don points out that sensitive people are often in conflict with society. I tell the men they seem like rebels and dreamers to me and that is probably what got them into trouble. There is beauty in their sensitivity, though it must be hard to remember that here. And then I ask them not to forget that specialness and to respect it. They listen quietly. They seem to drink the words.

I go on to talk to them about the end of the term that we are all so aware of. "It doesn't really matter that there won't be a class next term," I say, "because we have had this time together. You can continue now with what we have begun . . . not only the writing but the sharing." The men remain silent. I feel they have somehow known I was going to say these words and have been waiting to receive them.

Greg breaks the silence finally. He has brought in more journal entries and has also begun a long autobiographical story entitled "The Ranch of my Past." He describes growing up on a large ranch. He spent all his time damming up a pond to create a smaller one. Then he would fish in the larger pond and carry the fish in a bucket to release them in his own small pond. When he wasn't fishing, he would be busy bringing food to feed the fish, worms he had dug up and scraps from the family meals:

> . . . And then I found I was real fond of a wildflower called a Tiger Lily. And so I would work my tail off digging the bulbs up. They grew deep into the ground and I can remember they seemed to be always in hard and rocky spots. I planted my bulbs all around my pond. In the spring I had a colorful pond which I had to show my mom. She too liked my flowers and so I went on a hunt for more. When I found some I would spend hours digging them up for my mom and she lined the walk with them.

He is excited about his writing and how much more he has to tell. He predicts that when he finally leaves camp he will have volumes of writing to take with him.

There is still time left and I pass around a bag of fortune cookies. I ask the men to write a story or a poem that the fortune suggests to them. They laugh and agree to try that during the week. And Jeff, of course, gets the extra cookies.

Before we leave, I talk to David about the class and give him paper and a pen and the poems I handed out at the start of the term. He has been quiet all evening but attentive. He says he will try to write something for next week. "But go easy on me," he pleads and we assure him we will.

Tom and Jeff agree to take books for Miguel and messages from me. He has been absent for the last two weeks and I am still hoping we can convince him to return. And then the men leave slowly, stopping to thank me for coming and for bringing the books. "We appreciate you," Jeff says looking embarrassed.

Robert and I walk to the door together. He asks again when the class will end. He will be released at the end of January, a few weeks after the ending of the class. I tell him I will be excited about his release. He says he guesses he will too but he isn't sure where he should go or what he should do. We walk outside and say goodnight. There is a telephone just outside the guard station and a prisoner I do not know is talking earnestly. The rain is beating down.

DECEMBER 11

It is a clear moonlit night as I drive to camp. The men arrive one by one. Miguel comes in smiling. "The men said I had to come," he tells me. And I smile and tell him I am glad he is back. Greg appears in the doorway. He works as the camp butcher and has work to do. He says he will try to come later. Dave returns tonight but hasn't written anything. In fact few of the men have written anything during the week. But Tom and Reuben go off to copy what there is.

Reuben has written some small poems. He was attempting to write in the form of linked verse, an old Japanese form I had told him about. But he got confused about the form:

> Door swings wide open
> An eagle soars in the sky
> Lily pads sleeping lightly
> A desert prays shade

I suggest he turn it into a haiku:

> A door swings open
> An eagle soars in the sky
> A desert prays for shade

His poems are always evocative:

> Night becomes very still
> thunder is heard far away
> Spiders set their silky threads
> All wait for the morning

The men have little to say tonight. The mood of these Thursdays, as each man reads aloud his work, is serious and sometimes almost reverent. But tonight seems more like a group of reluctant schoolboys.

Tom is breaking into laughter about almost anything. Somehow the mood doesn't bother me. Perhaps it is preparation for the ending of class. Or maybe because most of the men haven't brought any writing, they feel detached. The intensity of the evenings can be painful. We may all be in need of something light.

Jeff has brought a short piece, almost a prose poem. He describes playing baseball with a friend and breaking a window. The only witness is his little brother. They try bribing him:

> . . . I'll give you my baseball I said. No. Then what about
> my baseball and my new glove, my friend Sherman added.
> No. Well what do you want. I want to tell.

And then Robert reads a long moving poem entitled "The Sad Snow":

> My snow floated beautifully, languidly . . .
> Gravity let it down, slowly and gently
> It was all in silence
> This grand huge thing happening . . .
> It was all done silently
> but it seemed to be as to music . . .
> and I was glad that this veil of whiteness
> was all around me. Because I could
> hide my face from other people. Because
> I didn't want them to see my sorrow . . .
> And in this sorrow, I saw the true
> beauty of the snow. I felt sorrow
> for the snow and I didn't want to
> go inside.

I make a few small suggestions and talk to Robert for awhile about writing. This poem pleased him when he wrote it, but then he went through a period of doubt about it.

We talk about how often that happens with any writer. He has read a great deal. I already know he likes Henry Miller and Steinbeck. Now he talks of Eldridge Cleaver and William James and Thoreau. He doesn't have the kind of books he wants available to him here. And he misses them.

Robert also writes the first few pages of a story. In it a man is moving into an apartment with his girlfriend and they find a checkbook from her uncle's company has turned up in one of the cartons they are unpacking. It takes only a moment for them to set off to cash the checks, knowing they will use the money to buy drugs. As the men talk about the story, they all seem familiar with writing illegal checks. I wonder how many of them have done this and then spent the money for drugs. And I wonder how Robert can resist doing it again when he is released. The mood of the couple when they find the checks is jubilant, even though they are aware they will probably be caught.

Greg comes in. He has finished working and is ready to rejoin the group. He hasn't brought any writing and so I give the men an exercise to try, hoping it will stir their imaginations. I provide them with a sentence to use as an opening for a story: "And then after six years he saw her." They quickly begin writing.

After we take a break, the men begin reading what they have written. It is the first time that Miguel has handed something in. It helps me to understand the problems he is struggling with:

> Today after so many years of don't see her, finally I meet
> her. I know she still live on me. Today as for me I would like

embrace you like yesterday and kiss her lips only my
sometime in the past . . .

We go through it slowly. He is so eager to learn this cumbersome
language that I don't think it will take him very long.

Tom describes seeing his daughter after many years:

> She was beautiful with her long brown hair and brown eyes
> staring at me with her mouth wide open not saying a word.
> It was like we both had seen a ghost . . .

Greg has written a love story:

> . . . She is standing there in front of me looking at me. She
> must see how the time has worn heavy on my face and my
> grayish hair . . .

David writes a little story with a surprise ending. And Don writes
about a man visiting his grandmother. He tells us he recently wrote
to his grandmother telling her he was at camp. He had delayed as
long as he could. Her response was warm and understanding. And
Jeff too says it was hard to explain to his grandmother. But she was
kind when he finally did.

Everyone had felt they must finish their stories in the little while
they had, and of course there wasn't enough time. Perhaps one of
the men will like his writing well enough to develop it during the
week. We all agree that writing in class doesn't really work. There
isn't enough time and there isn't the privacy that is needed.

Class has ended and everyone gathers up their papers. Robert is the
last to leave the room. I can tell how much he would like to talk.
Conversation between us is slow to unfold and there is not time

enough for it nor place. We try anyway but it is awkward. I ask him if he has thought about going back to college when he is released. His love of literature and of writing seem deep. And perhaps he would like the people he would meet. He murmurs that he hasn't ever thought about it but that it is a possibility. He mentions that he would be older than the other students but he knows that doesn't really matter. As we talk we are walking toward the door. I tell him again how beautiful I found his poem. He thanks me and we say goodnight.

DECEMBER 18

I drive out to camp tonight with brownies and cookies. I asked permission last week from the officer on duty and he granted it. I arrive early and park in the clearing. It is a still, foggy night. The silence is broken only by a few logging trucks rumbling by. I wonder what the mood of the men will be tonight with the holidays so near.

The guard announces class and the men arrive. Tom comes only to say he cannot attend class tonight because he was ill and didn't work today. David is absent and Reuben has to work in the office. The men describe a hard week. In the office a man is waiting to be transferred to the county jail. Two other men have also been *rolled up* this week.

Jeff is considering transferring to another camp. One of the guards is eager to trap him in some misdeed, he tells us. If the tension mounts too high, that is his only option. The men talk in a resigned way about the harassment of the guards. During fire season the men are needed and there is less chance of getting *rolled up*. But the fire season is over and the guards are paid overtime to transfer the men to another camp or deliver them to a jail.

Don and Greg have brought a few pages of journal entries tonight. Nobody else has had time or even the urge to write this week. Journal writing has come to mean a lot to these two men. Don had been keeping a journal before the class, and Greg began one in the last few months. And I am sure they will both be writing in their journals long after class has ended. For Greg especially, who has years more to serve, I think the writing will be a big help. He writes:

> . . . My cat has just climbed up on my lap to be patted and now he is up on my writing table moving my arm with his hand. Don weighed him last week and he is now sixteen pounds . . . I am glad to have him here with me. He has listened to me bitch about my time, but he never says a thing about his time here. And he listens to me more than most of the people here. Sure wish he could cook.

Don writes about the holiday season:

> After chow I stopped to talk to Skeet. He spoke of Christmas past here and at other camps where the camp gets into the spirit of the season. The conversation led us to the joint effort of decorating the tree. I made a point to choose ornaments which it appeared had been made by people who were here past Christmases. You know how each of us has definite ideas about how to go about decorating. Skeet is the first person I met who shortens a tree too tall for the room by cutting off the top rather than the bottom.

For the rest of the evening we eat cookies and brownies and just talk. Don shows the men a book called We *Are All Doing*

Time which is offered free to any inmate. It is a guide to higher consciousness which discusses meditation and diet and yoga. And it includes samples of the many letters the writer has received from prisoners and his responses to them. The men are interested in the book.

It turns out Jeff has spent a few years studying Scientology. He stopped when he finally realized how brainwashed he felt. He also speaks of numerology. His girlfriend studied it and he found the information she gave him amazingly accurate. Don talks about a psychic reading he once received that predicted clearly many things that have come to pass in his life. We talk on about the *I Ching* and the work that Ram Dass is doing with the dying. And we talk about the book *Life After Life* which records the stories of people who have been considered medically dead. They all speak of an experience of light and beauty which they are reluctant to give up in exchange for being brought back to life. Robert listens quietly. When I question him, he says he thinks all of that stuff is bunk.

The men go on talking about dreams and the symbols in dreams. I tell them about the Senoi tribe, a peaceful Maylasian group whose culture is centered around dreams and learning to direct their dreams. And we talk of yin and yang and darkness and light. Greg says that recently he keeps seeing his own darkness and the darkness of others. And he speaks of seeing the light.

And the men tell prison stories. They describe escapades and practical jokes, fires that have been set as a prank to startle an inmate in his cell of cement. They tell of drugs that seem to get smuggled into any prison. The stories go on and on. At first I am nervous when I hear them. It seems important that the men be very careful for the next few weeks. But I realize they are venting their anger and frustration. The guards strip away their self respect and their pride and as they tell their stories I think they

begin to feel whole again. I hope it will help them feel strong
enough to withstand whatever comes next.

Greg says he was talking to the lieutenant and asked about all the
racial tension. Why not divide the camps into separate racial and
ethnic groups, he suggested. The lieutenant responded grimly that
he didn't want all that tension directed at him.

The men talk about the harassment and victimization by the
guards. They feel guards at maximum security prisons are more
restrained for they know the retaliation of the prisoners there
would be swift. Then the men tell me that Karen, the other woman
instructor, has just learned she won't be teaching here next term.
She was scheduled to teach a class in remedial English. I wonder
what is going on. I think of the guard who interfered with both of
our classes and wonder if he has something to do with the fact that
neither of us will be here next term. And I wonder how the men
survive here in this place where there are no answers to questions,
only dark uncertainties that seem to hover in the air like ghosts.
The men have told me I have no idea how bad it is. They are
constantly being tested and pushed in the hopes that they will reach
a breaking point.

I finally glance at my watch and realize that class should have ended
awhile ago. None of us really want to leave. But we must. As we
depart, a guard immediately reclaims the room, opening all the
windows and complaining that we have fogged them up.

JANUARY 9

I drive out to camp through dense patches of fog. The guard announces the class. Jeff is the first to arrive. He has made it through the last few weeks without mishap. But Tom hasn't. Jeff tells me he has been sent to a camp that is further north. To the men, north means being further from family and the visitors they long to see.

Miguel is here tonight and Don and Reuben and Robert. David only came to two of the classes and I guess he won't be back. We ask the guard to page Greg but he doesn't appear. I have brought a huge pile of magazines. The men are pleased to find copies of *Alaska* magazine.

No one has written much. They mention that the last few weeks were difficult but they don't linger on the subject. Don reads some journal entries and Jeff has written an amusing piece about his eagerness for Christmas that begins around July. And Reuben writes a simple story in which the narrator is a lamppost. There is little to say about any of the stories and soon the room falls silent.

Jeff begins to talk about a strange dream that he has had again and again. He enters the dream just before dropping off to sleep. The story unfolds with each new dream. I ask if he would like to write about the dream and he says that he would. Robert and Don both have something they want to write. I ask Miguel if he will try to translate a few of the stanzas from the poem he has written in Spanish about his mother cooking tortillas. After I assure him that we will help him, he starts eagerly writing. Reuben isn't sure what to write and I make a number of suggestions hoping one of them will feel right to him. He likes the thought of beginning a story as a man boards a bus and throws his coins in the coin-box.

As the men begin to write I can tell that something good will result. A silence falls over the room. Jeff looks in the dictionary again and again. And Miguel searches the thesaurus for the words he can never seem to find. It is perhaps half an hour later that the men put down their pens. Reuben makes copies for us.

Jeff reads first about his dream. He has titled the piece "Dreams are Forever" or "This Dream Forever Forever More":

> . . . Every night after everyone is asleep, I find myself going down to the basement through a little black door that leads me into this long and narrow cold cave beneath the house where all the money is at. And every night I add a little bit more to the sack of bills. First to the $90,000 until I have $100,000 total. Then I add the $100,000 to the millions of dollars which are already there. Until I reach 100 million. Then I add that to the sack of billions of dollars to infinity.

The men chuckle appreciatively at the dream. But Jeff is deeply puzzled by it. He says he thinks the money means more than simply money. I tell him I have never known anyone to have a dream that unfolds night by night. What a deep feeling it must be expressing.

Reuben's character has gotten on the bus and found himself with two girls on opposite sides of the aisle. He has difficulty choosing between them. He finally makes a decision:

> . . . I find her sweet, charming and intelligent. I mentioned to her the dilemma that I had encountered a few seconds before in deciding where to sit down and what had passed through my mind. She laughed wickedly and said, "Why don't I introduce you to my friend across the aisle." The three of us got to know each other rather well and they let me in on their game. They would sit opposite on purpose

and the one who would have more guys sitting next to her at the end of the month would be treated to dinner by the other.

He is pleased with his story and eager to write more. We both express the wish that the term were not ending. And yet perhaps the natural form of a cycle is to end at a beginning.

Don has continued with the journal:

> . . . The arrival of this new year brings encouragement of things to come and the frustration of waiting six more months to walk the streets. It is now a time to work even harder on achieving the goals I put before myself while institutionalized. I'm satisfied that now, after Christmas, this work is taking place.

> Since Christmas running is again a daily event with some of the stretching exercises. Relief of stress and a clear mind to study in the morning is the result.

He talks about how he keeps scribbled notes of things he wants to write. Sometimes it is days before he gets the chance to write about them in the journal.

Next Miguel reads his poem aloud:

Mama's Hot Plate

> I recall that particular hot plate
> how can I forget it
> if at his side usually I used to sit down
> to see my mother cooking

Grind on her old flat stone
grinding the boiled corn
preparing my daily meal
the one has fortified me

Listen to the sound of her hands
she makes to the tortilla shape up
I used to sit down at her side
with uncommon appetite . . .

. . . At the end of her morning labor
calling everybody for breakfast
Come taste, come eat
the tortillas of Mama

Together we help him to correct the English. And the struggle he
has in translation becomes clear. The stove his mother cooks on is
a woodstove. And she cooks on the circular plate in the center.
None of us can come up with the word, and we doubt that there is
one. Someone finally suggests *griddle*. We agree that it is closer than
hot plate but none of us are really satisfied. There is a charm and
sensitivity in the words Miguel does find. And I try again to convince
him. He promises to bring the last two stanzas next time. And I
think he is beginning to realize that he does better than he thinks.

Next Robert reads a new poem entitled "Ode to the Morning." It
begins in the morning silence and the mist and chill. And then:

Birds sing the sun to rise above the trees
And celebrate the accomplishment of their deed
And they all come and rejoice at my coronation
For they are all glad that I am crowned
king of the morning.

I suggest a word change here and there. Robert listens attentively. And after awhile he laughs his husky laugh and says he doesn't agree. I feel like I have overstepped a boundary. There is beauty in the poem and I think Robert wants that acknowledged. For now that is all that he wants. And the poem deserves it. It celebrates and sings.

Greg comes in as we are all preparing to leave. He hasn't had much time to write. Truckloads of salmon have been arriving and it is his job to clean them all. He was asleep and even the paging didn't wake him. He reads us a poem written by his friend but no one responds. The men are already getting up and beginning to walk around. For some reason we are all suddenly tired. Greg seems to understand. He looks very tired himself.

After class Reuben stays to talk. He has always felt restricted, he tells me, and suddenly he feels very free to write fancifully, to let his imagination run free. "It's a wonderful feeling," he says.

And Jeff and I walk out together into the rain. He talks more about his dream and his yearning to understand it. And he talks about wanting to learn to meditate. He wants to stay out of trouble. So far there are no marks against him and his quiet serenity is presenting a challenge to the guards. He has a year more to serve and hopes that by moving to another camp he can protect himself. And then he dreams aloud about his release. "I want to start an animal clinic when I am free or perhaps I'll be a writer. I never was on the streets. There are men here who want to come back but I don't want to. I just made a stupid mistake." I wonder if the guards will notice us standing here together and insist that I leave. "You seem very psychic," I tell Jeff. "Yes," he says, "I know. I sometimes know what someone is thinking."

I drive off slowly in the rain. When I reach home I'm confused to find it is an hour later than usual. Class must have lasted for four hours. No wonder we were all so tired at the end.

January 15

The days are growing longer. I sit across from camp in the gathering twilight. And then I slowly drive in.

Skillet, the camp dog, greets me as I enter. He follows me into the classroom. Tonight I bring a platter of cookies and three boxes of books that the bookstore has donated. A prisoner I don't know helps me carry things in. One of the guards who has always been reserved makes mocking comments. Perhaps the largesse annoys him. But I am feeling so at home here tonight that I hardly notice. I do not bother to ask permission for bringing the books or the cookies. The time for that seems past.

Skillet follows me into the room, and as I arrange all the books on the table, I feed him cookies. The men arrive and begin to browse through the books. Miguel asks me about *War and Peace* and I tell him about it. "I have much time to read," he tells me. And he takes the thick book happily back to his seat.

I give Robert *Wuthering Heights.* He has never read it and I have a feeling he might cherish it. Jeff and Reuben choose two Shirley McLaine books. They have heard about them. Greg seems uninterested. I would have thought he was a reader but he takes only *The Guinness Book of Records.* The men go on choosing until each has a small stack of books.

Only a few of the men have brought writing tonight. Reuben brings a rather formal essay about scuba diving. And Greg brings eight pages that describe an ice-fishing trip:

> . . . and I fell asleep and was awakened to the sounds of geese flying over me. It was very strange to hear the geese at night. To this day I still can't believe that they can and do fly in the darkness of the snowy mountain lake . . .

This man seems to have a flood of wilderness images within him just beginning to be released.

Jeff has brought a few pages entitled "The End":

> . . . time has grow short. It seems only yesterday we started the class. I am proud to say I have enjoy this open work-shop. I have appreciate the time, the effort and acknowledge the understanding, the friendship, also the laughters, the cookies that Judy has share with us . . .

I can tell how rushed the writing must have been by the errors. It is the first time I have seen a mistake in Jeff's careful writing. I see now he has worked much harder than I realized. The men talk for a few moments about how much they agree. I thank them.

They have all been awaiting my reading from the story I have written about the camp. I have brought the seal story as well and mention it. No one responds. I think it was only Tom who longed to hear it. I find I am glad for it seems right that the evening end with the writing of the men. I have told them that I will read aloud all the passages I have quoted from their writing. Greg asks if I will also read the sentences that introduce each passage and I agree.

And then I read. Robert keeps his head down but now and then I can see his slow smile. The others meet my eyes whenever I look up. I see Jeff glancing at his papers when I read from his work. I think he is making certain that I quote him correctly. As I read we all are reminded of how many men have come and gone through the weeks. They seem to return for a moment.

Now and then my eyes fall on a passage from the story itself that seems right to read to them. Tom's name comes up and we smile. I am not sure but I think we are smiling at his youthfulness and his tenderness and what a hard road may be ahead of him. As I read I grow cold and notice that my hands are trembling. And I notice the silence of the men and how deeply they are listening.

Afterwards the men ask questions. Robert asks where I will submit the story and thinks my choice is a good one. They ask if I will let them know if it gets published. We finally agree that they should pass around a paper on which everyone will write down an address away from camp. None of us want to call the story to the attention of the officials here. They are aware that I will change their names and at first they are as reluctant as I am to conceal their identity. But we all realize it would be wiser.

And I suddenly realize from the excitement in the room that we may have won a round. For we have found a way that allows the men's writing to be published. The worst consequence might be my not being permitted to teach again at the camp. But that seems unlikely. And my future here is uncertain even now.

And then for a last few moments we talk. Robert will be released in a week and I ask him if he has decided what he will do. He shakes his head no. "I think you'll be a teacher," Greg says to him. And Robert goes on smiling silently. I talk to Jeff about his dream. I suggest that he keep thinking about each image in the dream and the feelings they arouse. In this way he may gradually come to understand it better. And Greg talks about the workshop. "It's the only time since I've been here that I don't feel like a prisoner," he says. The others say they feel this way too. I tell them that I am glad and I urge them to take more classes. For I know the other instructors and I am sure they would treat the men with respect.

I have brought letters for them and now I give them out. Robert goes out to the guard to get me the address of the camp where Tom has been sent. Jeff tells me he has a last question. "How did you like this class," he wants to know. I answer that I liked it more than any class I have ever taught. And then I tell them I will miss them. There is a warm murmur in response.

The end has come and none of us try to postpone it. I think we all sense a completion. We walk outside together and one by one the men shake my hand and walk away. Jeff is the last to leave. He calls back to me from the darkness, "I'm going to cry." "I am too," I call after him. But I do not cry. I drive home slowly along the bright moonlit roads.

Journey

She got in her car and headed north. It was evening and the sky was turning red and crimson. She pulled over to the shoulder of the road and watched the sun falling into the sea. The sky and the sea were crying.

She got in her car and headed north. Far across the country her father was dying. She called each day. It didn't help to call. Her mother was pieced together with paste and string and parts of her kept clattering down. Her father seldom came to the phone. Again and again she offered to come but her parents asked her to wait.

She got in her car and headed north. She was going to an island in Washington. She didn't know which island it would be. She was looking for a cabin at the water's edge. She was looking for eagles.

She lay on her bed in California. She hadn't left yet. She was staying at a friend's. She lay on the bed and waited. She wasn't sure what she was waiting for. She dreamed she had found a house. She could see it there across a wide meadow. There was a wild bull in the meadow and she was afraid to walk there.

She got in her car and headed north. She had lived on northern islands before. She remembered the long summer twilight. In winter the darkness swept down like a raven.

She got in her car and headed south. After a few miles she pulled over on the shoulder of the road. She gazed at the ocean on a morning in early October. She sat there motionless for a long time. She pulled back onto the highway and this time she headed north.

At night she coughed. Something had been caught in her throat for a week. She peered into the mirror and saw a moth with a torn wing.

She had been in Greece when she learned that her father was dying. She had walked home in the darkness along a narrow path above the sea. There was a note beneath her door in perfect English. She never found out who left it there. As she read the note, two sheep walked past her open door.

She got in her car and headed north. She sang along with the radio. She kept the window open. Sometimes she felt that she was dying too. Sometimes she felt her bones were small and not yet formed.

On her last night in Greece she rode on the back of a motorcycle through the streets of Athens. The wind was warm and she held on tightly to Konstandis. He had met her at the ferry and strapped all her luggage on the back of his bike. She could see the lights of the harbor as they wove in and out of traffic. Do you like to go fast, he called back to her. Yes, she answered, yes.

She returned from Greece to be with her father. She accompanied him when he went to the hospital for a blood transfusion. She held his hand and tried to warm it. Sometimes they talked and sometimes he dozed. She brought him a large piece of watermelon from the cafeteria. He loved watermelon and smiled as he ate it.

She stayed for about a week at her parents' apartment. Visitors were arriving from everywhere. She wasn't needed. She flew to

California, to a small coastal town where she had lived for years. It was filled with tourists now and it was hard to find a rental. She checked the paper each day. There were a few small dark apartments. She reluctantly agreed to rent one. The depression that followed surprised her. She apologized and backed out of the agreement. She stayed with a friend. Her life seemed in suspension. Her life seemed like a waiting room.

On her last night in Greece, she had a reservation at a hotel in Athens. Konstandis brought her there. He cradled her in his arms and they slept. His father was dying too.

She got in her car and headed north. I need a home, she thought. I need a place to rest. It felt elemental. She wanted a bookcase for her books. She wanted a bed and a chair and a desk. I'm fifty years old, she thought. All of my life I have been borrowing from others.

She felt better as soon as she began to pack. Her things had been in storage. Now she strapped a car carrier on top of her car and filled it with blankets and clothes. She arranged her boxes in the back of her car. The packing was like working on a puzzle. She wanted things in perfect order. She had felt tired and ill for weeks. Now she had a surge of energy. She lifted her file cabinet into the car. She felt as if she had had a transfusion.

Her father's cancer was responding to treatment. The doctors felt he had longer to live than the few months they had predicted. When she called her mother and father, they sounded peaceful. They were watching the Olympics on television. They talked and divers fell through the empty air.

She drove fast. She liked the simplicity of travel. She liked the anonymity of travel. As she drove she watched the waves spilling to shore below her. She spent the first night in a small motel. In the morning she climbed down to the beach. The moon still lingered in the sky. A layer of mist floated just above the sea.

She drove only a few hours each day. Then she wandered around whatever small coastal town she had stopped in. She browsed aimlessly through shops and sipped coffee and read the local newspaper in cafés. In one of the towns she walked into a realtor's office. She spent the afternoon with him looking at the houses that were for sale. That night she went running on the beach at sunset. Her motel had a sauna and she lay there watching the thermometer rise.

She got in her car and headed north. She was driving now through a deep forest on a lonely stretch of road. Suddenly an accident blocked her way. A woman was bleeding from the mouth and the ambulance hadn't yet arrived. A few people were gathered there trying to help. She pulled over on the shoulder and got out of her car. Someone handed her a baby to hold. The baby seemed unharmed. She stood on the side of the road rocking the baby in her arms. It gazed up at her peacefully. After awhile it fell asleep.

She reached Washington just as autumn began. She waited for the ferry. The water was blue and the air had turned crisp. She stood shivering in the sunlight, thinking of a night in Greece. The flame of her candle had been too warm. She had blown it out and lain awake in the darkness and the heat. She didn't remember falling asleep, but when she opened her eyes a huge orange sun was lifting out of the sea.

She called her father. He sounded weary and frightened. He was having trouble catching his breath. The doctors were recommending now that chemotherapy be applied directly to his stomach. This required a surgical implant and careful monitoring. Let me come to see you, she said. I have a lot of love to give you, she said. I have a lot of love to give you also, he responded. His voice was tender. His voice was tired. And still he held her off.

She was on an island where several close friends lived. She wanted to spend time with them. And she wanted time to look around and choose a place to live. She rented a small cottage that was available for a few weeks. But there were other islands further from the mainland that drew her. She had been traveling for a long time. She wondered if she were almost home.

She dreamed she received a telephone call. It was an official informing her of the death of a seven-year-old girl. She didn't know the girl. She didn't understand why they were calling her. She hung up the phone and wept.

She opened a journal that she had kept in Greece. She read of sunlight and olive groves. She read of stony footpaths that wound over the mountains to a turquoise sea. Now she walked along a beach and the gray of the sky met the gray of the water. She felt as if she were walking in her sleep.

The rains had begun and she still hadn't found a place to rent for the winter. She revisited a city where she had once lived. Rain flooded the streets and all the car windows were fogged. She was looking for flannel pajamas for her father. She wanted them to be blue, the color of his eyes. She was looking for long underwear for him. His red blood count was low and he was always chilled. She got lost looking for the post office down the rain-drenched streets. She finally found it and mailed his package. All day she felt she had a purpose. Now she stood there, wet and foolish and empty-handed.

She visited a man she had once loved. He was seeing another woman now but he made her an omelette and listened to her pain.

That night she telephoned her father again and again. His surgery had taken place that morning and he should have been home hours ago. She felt as if she were crying deep inside where no one else could hear. She finally reached him. He was tired and discouraged and the place of the incision was sore.

She returned to her cottage. She met a man named Robert at the local tavern. The next day they met again and drove together down long wooded lanes. They visited his friends and sipped tea by the fire. She had been afraid of closeness, afraid something terrible would be revealed about her. Now everyone seemed like a lover.

She rode the ferry out among the islands. The weather turned suddenly warm. She sat on the deck and watched the forested islands. There were a few cabins along the shore and deep, green coves. Mountains rose out of the water and loneliness circled like a dark forgotten bird.

She remembered a dream of the night before. She had been flying. At first she thought it was the wind that was lifting her, that was carrying her. But even when she turned into the wind, she flew.

She got off the ferry and followed the line of cars up the narrow hill. She checked into a small inn. She bought a newspaper and called each place that was for rent. They had already been rented. She drove out to see one cabin. A man named Ed showed her around. He had promised the cabin to someone already, but would let her know if that didn't work out. They talked for awhile. He said he would look for her in town that night.

She checked into an inn. Then she found a place where she could house-sit for a few days. She opened a post office box. She opened a bank account. She called her father to tell him where she was but he was out of breath and couldn't speak to her. She told him she loved him. She told him she would come soon. When she hung up the phone, everything she was doing seemed deranged.

She spent that night with Ed. She had been celibate for years and waited for awkwardness or regret to follow. But she slept peacefully and woke in his arms. I feel like I've known you for a long time, he said. Yes, she answered, I feel that way too.

Her moods swung up and down like an axe. Her parents didn't want her to visit until she got settled. She looked at houses. There was a house in the woods she liked but it seemed very dark. There was a cabin on the water but she couldn't reach the owner. She drove to see it. She stood on the deck and gazed in the windows. She wanted to build a fire in the woodstove. She wanted to be inside sitting on the window seat. She called the owner again and this time he answered. She arranged to rent the cabin but it wasn't available for three more weeks.

Her brother called her. The cancer was spreading. Her father was in pain and they were talking about an operation. Her mother was lost and frightened and her father was drugged now and confused. The call came late at night. She slept and woke again and again struggling to find her way toward morning.

Early the next morning she called her parents. Her father had a 103 degree fever. They were leaving for the emergency room. She made a reservation to leave that night. When she arrived at dawn, her brother met her at the plane. The fever had broken. Her father was in the hospital but he was out of immediate danger.

Her father stayed in the hospital for a week receiving antibiotics intravenously. She stayed with her mother and each morning they drove to the hospital and stayed all day. She went to the utility room for extra blankets to cover her father with. She brought him a poetry book to read and a sketch pad and pencil. She placed them on the bed table and they made the room seem less sterile. But his days were taken up with thermometers and nurses, and meals which he ate very slowly. He had sores in his mouth and he was very weak. He told her to take the book and the sketch pad away.

After a week he was released from the hospital. She went to pick him up and bring him home. She went shopping with her mother. She cooked soup. She made milkshakes for her father to try to keep him from losing weight. Each day he seemed a little bit stronger.

It was November now but the warm days lingered. They went outside for slow walks together. She took him to his office one day and carried his briefcase up the long flight of stairs. She drove him to an art class and helped carry his paintbox and some paintings he had been working on. He hadn't been to class for months and had feared he would never be well enough to go again. He stayed for hours, standing and painting with a rapt expression on his face. The painting was an abstraction that swirled with colors. When the class was over he seemed bewildered. On the ride home he told her, If I could do that more often I might live for a long time.

She stayed for three weeks. She hoped the visit had been a help. Her father seemed stronger and she felt it was time to leave. She flew back across the country. The cabin was ready now. It was night when she turned the key and entered. A fire was laid for her in the woodstove.

Through the long solitary days she slowly unpacked her car and sent for the rest of her things. She took walks on the beach and looked for eagles. At night she dreamed of the shrill cry of crickets and the voices of shepherds calling to their goats. She dreamed of Nikos the crippled fisherman and Katarina with her brown luminous eyes. Birds kept falling from an azure sky.

Her father sent her a note. He said her departure had left him with a terrible emptiness. She telephoned and learned he had been running a fever again. Now his temperature was normal but he was in pain. He was weary and once again he was having trouble catching his breath.

She got in her car but there was nowhere to go. She was in the northernmost corner of the country. She was on the northern tip of the island. It didn't matter where she was. There was nothing she could do to keep her father from pain, to keep him from dying. She saw him walking away down a lonely corridor. Where are you going, she called. Where are you going, she pleaded. She sat there in the rain and the darkness and the silence.

PART II

Receiving

Greek Island Sketchbook

VOURAIKOS GORGE

I take a train along the coast of the Peleponnese, past small villages
with red tiled roofs strung out along the bright sea. I get off in a
small town where the narrow gauge railway originates. The little
train is already waiting there and ready to leave. I keep rushing from
window to window, wishing I could look everywhere at once. We
are riding through a deep narrow gorge and below is a clear rushing
river. On each side there are jagged hills and pines. The beauty
brings tears to my eyes.

⁓

The old hotel where I stay looks out over the river. Below my
window is a sea of greenery and high cliffs and birds singing. I cross
a small bridge and then walk the village paths. The villagers greet me
as I walk. Each house has a garden filled with flowers and vegetables.
Around a bend a sweet-faced toothless woman smiles at me. She is
sitting on the ground and crocheting. Beside her is a mother goat
and three fluffy kids. They are two months old, she tells me.

I ride the little train to the next town where the gorge opens into a wide valley surrounded by mountains. In 1943, all the men and boys of the village were killed and the town burned to the ground. There is a large memorial to the dead and the church clock is forever stopped at the hour of their death.

I walk the railroad tracks back to my hotel and sit on the banks of the river. The men and boys in this tiny village were also killed. It seems impossible that such bloodshed could happen amidst this sacred beauty.

I wake to a blue sky and streaming sunlight. I wake to the present. Below my window a little boy is happily shouting, Papa. Papa.

KOSMAS

I first heard of this little village high in the mountains many years ago. And now I sit in its square at a small café sipping a fresh orange juice. There are lush green trees everywhere. The maples are already turning yellow and orange. And then I walk each little lane with its lovely houses and views out over the mountainside. Far in the distance are a few more tiny villages nestled in the hills. And far far below is the sea. I would like to live in this village where the bus comes only once a week and time is measured only by the sun slowly crossing the wide blue sky.

Naxos

Outside my window is a garden of geraniums, a towering palm tree and then the ever-present sea. The veranda is enclosed with bamboo, a lemon tree with giant lemons and a plum tree.

⌒

I discover my toe has a huge blister. Just as I am walking along and wondering what to do about it, a thorn from a shrub I am passing pricks it open. I am a few doors from a market where I find disinfectant and a bandage.

⌒

As I walk along the beach, I see a woman sitting at the water's edge. She is arranging tiny shells on the back of her hand. I sit down beside her and together we admire the perfect shells and talk. Friendship can be so effortless among travelers. She comes from Tasmania and tells me about her life in that faraway land.

⌒

I go for a breathtaking bus ride over the mountains with hairpin turns and serpentine roads with long perilous drops. We pass lovely little mountain villages clinging to the hillsides. And then we descend to a tiny port on the northern edge of the island.

PAROS

I take a hotel room next to the busy port. I'm too tired to search any further. Little insects bite at me all night. The air is filled with the noise of a generator, cars and motorbikes roaring by and loud rock music from a nearby café. Unable to sleep, I go out on my balcony in the darkness. In the dirt yard below there are seven or eight hobbled goats. And I can just make out the shapes of many large fluffy rabbits hopping here and there among the sleeping goats. I sigh when I think of all the goat and rabbit I saw on the menus of the cafés.

I wander through a village by the sea. Small chapels are covered with bright bougainvillea. The lanes are filled with small cafés and shops and pots of flowers are on every balcony. Fish tavernas line the shore. Some fishermen sit outside a small seaside chapel and fold their golden nets.

It is a long hot climb to Petaloudhes, The Valley of the Butterflies. And then I find myself in a lush oasis of chestnut trees and fruit trees. The air feels tropical. The butterflies are almost invisible, resting on the leaves and branches of the trees. Here and there a few take flight, revealing the bright crimson on their wings. The butterflies are easily disturbed. Along the pathways there are graceful wooden signs decorated with painted flowers:

ΜΗΝ ΚΤΥΠΑΤΕ ΠΑΛΑΜΑΚΙΑ
Don't clap your hands.

ΜΗΝ ΚΟΥΝΑΤΕ ΤΑ ΚΛΑΔΙΑ
Don't shake the branches.

ΜΗΝ ΣΦΥΡΙΖΕΤΕ
Don't whistle.

This is a silent white village with archway after archway and flowers everywhere. Time stopped here long ago. I sit alone on the veranda of a tiny café that looks out over a wide expanse of fields falling away to a few small villages far below. And beyond that is the sea.

IRAKLIA

I board a small boat called the Skopeletis. It is packed with goods for the islands it visits. The space left for passengers is small and we are crowded together on the upper deck. It is a wild windy ride. As we near the island there are dolphins everywhere, their backs rising above the water. Not a pod swimming together, but dolphins swimming singly in all directions. We enter the small harbor and the air is filled with the sweet scent of herbs.

The sunset turns the sky and the sea to lilac and crimson and orange. I walk through the little village in the deepening darkness. At last I realize I don't know the way back to my room. An older man and his wife are sitting quietly on their veranda. I hesitate to disturb their privacy but finally I quietly approach them. The man smiles when I tell him I am lost. He is wearing pajamas but he comes with me and kindly points my way home.

～

The village school is visible from my veranda. Each afternoon the school children gather outside to dance. There will be a public performance in a few days. I listen to the music and watch their graceful circle.

～

It is astonishingly hot. I set out with friends on a long walk to the Chora, the oldest village of the island. We carry large bottles of water. We lose the footpath and end up scrambling up goat paths, descending and climbing endless ravines. After a few hours we can see the white village gleaming in the distance but we don't know how to reach it. We can't find a path and again and again we find ourselves stopped by walls or deep ravines. At last we are sure we will be there in only a few moments but we find ourselves suddenly standing before another deep ravine. Hot and tired, we finally arrive. The views are hauntingly beautiful with the sea stretched out far below.

～

Before I sleep I climb through my window onto the veranda. The moon is setting over the islands. There is an otherworldly quality here, silent and ghostly and eternal.

KOUFONISSI

The sea here has the colors of the Caribbean, a soft turquoise and uncountable blues. Behind the port where most of the tourists stay is a lively little village filled with children. They are dark-skinned and have a wild gypsy look.

⌐

Tonight as I step into my shower, I find there is no hot water. And the water that spills over me tastes of salt.

⌐

I wander down the road along the shore and find a small boat harbor with a few small tavernas that are closed, for it is still early in the season. I sit in the shade of a fishing boat pulled up on the beach. A flock of sheep suddenly appears in a nearby field. I watch them climb effortlessly over an old stone wall.

⌐

I find a little café that is open and stop for a coffee. There is beautiful old pottery set in recesses in the wall and the stone benches are covered with richly colored woven blankets. The woman who brings me my coffee also presents me with a wonderful fruit and cream tart. Below is an old abandoned windmill. The sea is blue-green with deep purple shadows.

～

I find my landlady Sophia in her garden. A boat with fresh water for the island has just arrived and she is watering her flowers and vegetables. In the garden are cilantro, *horta,* tomatoes, cosmos, violets, geraniums, and dahlias. The names in Greek are almost the same as in English. I help her water and we chat. Her friends come and go. A few children stop by to visit with her. Her warmth seems to attract everyone.

～

In the evening, the electricity fails. I go to find Sophia to ask for candles for my room. Instead she gives me a lovely old oil lamp. As I walk home along the beach I am dazzled by the stars, more stars than I have ever seen. The Milky Way is a path of light spilling across the sky.

HYDRA

I have visited this island many times. Today I walk along the shore, passing the beautiful mansions that rest just above the sea. Cruise ships glide by, leaving a turquoise wake in the azure sea.

The shopkeepers still remember me and greet me. I stop to talk to the baker who used to give me cookies when I came in the mornings to buy a fresh loaf of bread.

⌒

Pantelis drives the garbage truck. We sit in a café and sip a glass of wine. His donkey Loulouka waits patiently beside a tree. Each time Pantelis says her name, she turns to gaze at him. And finally she lifts her head and gives a long heartrending bray.

⌒

This morning as I sit in my doorway, three men pass by shouting out their wares. One has a cart filled with roosters, one has hens and a large basket of tiny yellow chicks. The last cart is piled high with plastic tables and chairs. The villagers come out to look over the wares. Donkeys walk by, their hooves clattering on the cobblestone street. Cats climb on the red tiled rooftops.

⌒

I walk many miles to a little hamlet in the hills. It's the first time I've seen these pine forests and rich greenery. And then I continue climbing to the peak of the mountain. I have crossed the island and far below me I can see the sea on the other side.

A strange warm wind blows all day. And tonight I have dinner at Katarina's café. She tells me there was an earthquake this afternoon, large enough to shake her house. I had been on the beach and one large unexpected wave startled everyone. We grabbed our things and ran halfway up the beach. I eat on the rooftop and watch a full moon emerge from the clouds. And then the rain begins and I move inside. When it is time to leave, I hesitate in the doorway and watch the pouring rain. Katarina notices me there and brings me her umbrella for the walk home.

The nights enchant me. I sleep by a deep-set open window. I hear the scops owl calling its high plaintive note. The cicadas sing and now and then a donkey emits a startling bray. The town clock chimes the hours. At first light the roosters begin crowing. And soon a chorus of children's voices sings out like a flock of small birds greeting the dawn.

There is a monastery in the mountains that is visible from the port. I climb a footpath winding up and up. The road snakes back and forth beneath a forest of pine. Just as I am ready to give up, I come to a small sign for the monastery. And in another few kilometers I come to a gate. And then there is a long flight of stairs, so long that I almost turn back. But at last I reach the monastery. The small chapel is locked and the main building has its door closed. There is a knocker, but I am content to remain outside. I sit in a large *alóni,* a threshing floor, looking out over a dazzling view of the Peleponnese and its deeply shadowed hills. A few thin cats roam the grounds. A pen of chickens and roosters. Goat bells ring softly in the distance. And stillness, such stillness.

A large ship is unloading its goods at the port. Refrigerators, washing machines, cases of every kind of food, heaters and lumber and huge sacks of rice. The unloading takes hours. About a dozen men work and many of us have gathered to watch. There are no cars on this island. Soon things will be loaded into large carts and donkeys will haul them away.

Rain and thunder and lightning. The trees and flowers shed their dusty coats. Each lane becomes a river of rushing water. The island is washed clean.

I have dinner at Katarina's restaurant and afterwards we chat. She plans to close the café for a few months. She tells me in the winter she likes to walk in the mountains picking herbs and mushrooms. I like imagining her there in the mountains. Here in the café she looks so frail and works so hard.

She is wearing a lovely woolen skirt and sweater. When I compliment her on them, she tells me she made them herself about ten years ago. Each evening she and her mother and her grandmother would sit talking. They would sew and knit together until late at night.

SPETZES

I've come here by hydrofoil to spend only a day. I take a walk along the shore to the old port of Ayia Marina. The sun sheds its light everywhere and the sea is many colors of blue. I come to a park by the sea where I find charming black metal sculptures. There are bulls with long horns. And goats with long chains for their beards and udders. Some of the animals have bells for testicles. Two goats have their front feet resting against the trunk of a tree and appear to be nibbling the leaves. And of course perched near the sea and gazing out is a *gorgóna,* a mermaid.

ITHAKI

The ferry ride is a dream of mist and deeply forested islands. The Ionian sea is blue and green and golden.

⟿

I find a narrow rocky footpath that follows the coast and finally reaches a long pebbled beach. And then I take my first swim in this warm misty sea.

⟿

A man tells me about a huge earthquake that happened in the 1930s. The village was destroyed and the villagers had no food. Airplanes came and made drops of food. The villagers watched the food land in the treetops. Recovering it was long and difficult.

⟿

A friend arrives and we rent a motorbike to explore the island. The road hugs the coast and then winds higher and higher. We pass herds of black goats in the road. And suddenly a group of huge cattle block our way. We weave very slowly among them—mothers with their calves and the fierce looking long-horned bulls. They eye us warily but continue with their slow walk.

⟿

This village spills down the mountainside with beautiful old houses and ancient churches and dusty lanes. I climb to a monastery high above and look out to sea. Stretched out below are green mountainous islands in a sea of mist.

⁓

I ride on a small excursion boat. The man who works on the boat wants to marry me. Then I will be American and you will be Greek, he tells me. We will have two countries. Another man agrees to be our *kombári*. I tell him that once we are married I will ride each day on the boat with him. The boat stops in a cove and all of us climb down a ladder to swim in the turquoise sea.

⁓

I follow a footpath back from the beach. It is a long hot climb and I have made the mistake of not carrying water today. I come to a junction where I can take a path to the left or go straight. I go straight and keep on climbing. I'm hot and thirsty and realize finally that this path won't lead me to the village. I finally pass a house and catch sight of a woman inside. She comes out to greet me. She invites me in for water and coffee and biscuits. Her name is Olympia and she and her husband are fishermen. We visit for a long time and then she walks a little way with me to make sure I know the way back.

⁓

Along the footpath I pass a huge flock of goats. They are behind a fence, standing on their hind legs and nibbling at the olive trees. A few goats have gotten free and wander before me along the path.

In the village where I am staying there is a huge rock with a commemorative plaque celebrating the capture of a Nazi vessel by the Greeks in 1944. Today is the anniversary of that battle and about a hundred people have gathered. In front of the rock is a table with a gold embroidered tablecloth covered with large bouquets of flowers. A priest conducts a service and then everyone dines together at a café. Passionate music fills the air. These are the survivors and the families of those who gave their lives.

As I stroll up the road an old man with only two gleaming gold teeth beckons to me. He guides me into a small building. He indicates that he is deaf but he can speak a little English. This is the town hall, he proudly tells me. The walls are lined with old photographs and maps. There are pictures of the village before the earthquake and a little library with a few shelves of books. And there is a small room set aside for the doctor. It is a hardship for the old people to have to travel to another village, so they have convinced the doctor to see them here once a week.

It is autumn and the days are still warm with a soft misty light falling over everything. I follow the lanes and visit with the villagers I meet along the way. A man tells me how beautiful it is here in the winter. In winter, he says, there is no wind. In the stillness it is possible to hear everything . . . to see forever.

Antiparos

Antiparos, everyone says, there is nothing there. It is too quiet. There is no life. Antiparos, go there for an hour or two. It will be enough. I take the small boat that crosses the narrow channel between Paros and Antiparos and arrive at the small port. I find a room in a pension that overlooks the harbor where fishing boats are swaying in the breeze. The edge of the water is lined with small cafés shaded by trees. They thrive on the water from the sea, a Greek woman tells me. They are called the salt trees, she says.

My room is simple. Two single beds side by side covered with rough clean sheets. Another sheet and blanket are folded at the bottom of each. There is a small desk and chair. A narrow balcony looks out over the blue sea.

I walk the village road. There are a few small shops selling straw mats for the beach, shampoo and postcards. There are little grocery stores and tavernas and cafés. There are even a few travel bureaus that sell maps of the island. There are no other villages. There is nowhere to go.

Antiparos, where the old men sit in the square and watch everything that happens in the village. They notice that I sometimes walk with a Greek named Emanuel. Mani, they call him. When I walk alone, they give me news of Mani in rapid Greek. Mani is sleeping, they say, and rest their hands on their cheeks to show me what they mean. Mani is not in the square tonight, they say, and look at me sorrowfully. I smile and nod my head.

There are children everywhere. They play jumprope and run through the streets. They carry their baby brothers and sisters in their arms. They are shy and will not answer when I say hello. The little girls wear dresses and the boys already have a masculine air. In Dami's restaurant, he and his chubby little brother are drinking beer. They touch glasses. *Yia sou,* they say to one another. The boy takes a tiny swallow and exhales loudly as if he loves it. My little brother is sometimes a lot of trouble but tonight I drink beer with him, Dami says.

Dami also has a sister named Eleni with soft brown eyes. She is eighteen years old and works in the restaurant. She speaks only a few words of English and I a few words of Greek. But each night she finds a few moments to study with me. I have a book that I carry that gives phrases in English and in Greek. We recite the names of the days together. You are welcome, she says again and again, trying to pronounce the *w* which is hard for her. I see you later, she says, each syllable like a strange taste in her mouth. Good, I tell her. *Kalá.* She does far better than I.

The streets are noisy. There is construction going on everywhere. The village seems to grow before my eyes. Dust and debris and the frames of unfinished buildings. There will be a moratorium on building soon, I am told. Work will only be permitted to continue on buildings that have already been started. Tractors roar along the narrow streets and people press against the houses to let them pass. Dust fills the air.

The tourists will be arriving soon and all over the village rooms are being readied. Every possible unused space becomes a room to let. Women sweep the dust from their doorways and whitewash the curving white lines of the streets. New signs appear each day and new shops open. The old people sit in their doorways. *Kaliméra,* I say softly to them as I pass. *Kaliméra,* they respond. An old man beckons me inside. *Éla, éla,* he says. Come. He disappears for a moment into the back of the house and returns holding out a cookie for me.

Antiparos, it is very small, they tell me. There is nothing to do there. There is nothing to see, they say. There is only the light that is like the first day of creation. There is only the sea that is peacock blue with shadows of purple and lilac and copper.

Tonight a full moon rises over the hills. What is good tonight, I ask Dami. Everything is good. Everything I make is good, he says in a gruff voice and then smiles his slow gentle smile. Soup, he tells me, taking the lid off the large pot so I can see. Tonight I make lentils. Very good. I tell him I would like to marry him so he will cook for me every night. Why not, he answers. Why not. I sit each evening at one of the tables in the small enclosed courtyard. A small white chapel forms one of the walls. Flowers cascade over the walls and calamari dangle from a line. Tonight there is a parachute floating over our heads. It feels as if we are being lifted slowly into the moonlit sky. Dami's family has placed it there for shade on the hot afternoons. But the neighbors have complained and the next day I see that they have had to take it down.

I meet a couple from Austria named Heinz and Heidi. We spend our days together. We swim to the small uninhabited islands and climb the smooth white rocks. When the sun is low in the sky, we swim home. We meet for dinner at Dami's and Mani finds us there. He is reading Somerset Maugham. Each night he recites a new story for us. He is an orator, pausing dramatically as he speaks. He is reading Sophocles. An artist, he tells us, and then waits until all our eyes meet his, an artist when he is creating does not quite touch the earth.

Dami sits with us when all the customers have been served. He brings a bottle of wine with him for us all. His little brother also comes to sit at the table. He is six years old and shows us that he already knows how to multiply. And Eleni comes to sit for awhile with us. We smile at one another. We gesture helplessly.

I walk the beaches and find tiny shells shaped like the horn of a unicorn. Your eyes, Heidi tells me, are beautiful. They open wide like the eyes of a child. Today we climb a high hill and sit leaning against a chapel wall protected from the wind. A shepherd comes by with his herd of goats and greets us as he passes. One baby goat becomes confused and stays with us. We stroke its soft white fur but soon it begins to bleat. The shepherd calls to it, *Éla, Éla.* It goes on bleating and finally he returns and carries it away in his arms. And we go on sitting in the sunlight in the silence. Below us lies the village and the sea and the islands bathed in a soft mist.

Heinz and Heidi are leaving. I run to the port to say goodbye. We have exchanged addresses and promised to visit. I stand on the deck and wave goodbye. And I remain here in Antiparos where the hours pass slowly. *Segá. Segá.* I learn to tell time by the sun. I walk the beaches and the narrow village streets.

The American, the old sea captain says as I pass. California, the old men say and nod knowingly. I have an uncle in California, a boy tells me and his eyes shine at the thought of the faraway land. He is hoping when he finishes high school, he will be allowed to go to the university. He wants to study to become a teacher. *Tourista,* the man in the bakery greets me. All day he sits on his porch and reads. *Vivlío,* I say to him, holding up my own book. *Vivlío, vivlío,* he responds.

I sit in the courtyard of a taverna and sip coffee and read. The Greek boy who works there comes to talk with me. He shows me a book in Greek about the Dadaists. He has read Ginsberg and Kerouac and Burroughs, he tells me. He wants to become a writer. He plays tapes by Leonard Cohen and the mournful music spills out into the blue day.

I lie on the beach and my body grows brown in the sun. The warm wind is a lover that follows me everywhere. I swim to the island and sunbathe on the rocks. At night I meet Mani for dinner. He is mourning a close friend who died a few months ago. And all day today, he tells me, he has had a headache. Perhaps it is the departure of Heinz and Heidi that has reawakened your sorrow, I say to him, and he agrees. We talk of how many people we will be meeting. They will come and go. We must learn to let them go lightly, I say.

I have had a dream about my father, Mani says to me. He died years ago and I have not dreamed of him until now. In my dream he was alive and looked very well. He was dressed fashionably and he was an architect. He was building a house. I think it is a good dream, I respond. Yes, Mani says, I think so too. When I woke, I wrote to my sister to tell her of the dream.

The days drift by. At the café I breakfast on bread and honey and coffee and watch the fishermen mend their nets. I walk for hours past donkeys grazing and chickens pecking in the weeds. Today I decide to walk to the caves of Antiparos. I follow the shore for a few miles. I come to the road that winds slowly upward and a footpath that seems to climb straight to the top. I choose the path and ascend slowly, stopping often to catch my breath. There is no sign of a cave. Instead I find a road winding down to the shore and follow it. Soon everything looks strangely familiar. I find myself back where I began. *Den birázi.* What does it matter. I walk slowly toward home.

At dinner I tell Mani about my visit to the caves and he laughs. Today he has no headache. He has had a good swim, he tells me, and a nap in the afternoon. Eleni comes to sit with us. She and

Mani speak in Greek. Do you have a boyfriend, he asks her. I think it is too soon for that, she responds. But tonight there is a wedding in the square and everyone has gathered. Music is playing and people are dancing. Eleni is working but now and then she finds a few moments to slip away. And I notice as she leaves that her walk becomes the walk of a woman. I will be her best man when she marries, Mani tells me proudly. She has promised me. Ah Eleni, Eleni, he says and rests his hand over his heart.

Later I walk home through the darkened streets. Tonight there is no electricity and the moon has not yet risen. Candles and gas lamps glow in all the windows. I find my way upstairs to my room with a lighted match. I sit on my balcony in the darkness and listen to the whisper of the sea.

Antiparos, where my sleep is broken into many pieces. Voices float up from the cafés, rising and falling and I sleep and wake. At last there are a few hours of silence. And then the sounds begin anew when the sun begins its long slow climb across the sky. Tractors rumble by and a truck selling mattresses or plastic chairs drives by loudly announcing its wares. The village women gather at dawn at the fishing boats to buy the catch. And all along the harbor the fishermen fling calamari against the cement. It is a sound that has grown familiar, the rhythm as steady as a metronome.

Today when I wake, something is different. Today I am leaving Antiparos. Eleni and I have kissed and said goodbye. Stay, she cried. Stay in Antiparos. Dami and I have shaken hands. And I have said goodbye to Mani and embraced him and we have wished each other well. He has friends arriving soon. If my departure saddens him, it will not be for long. I wash and dress and carry my luggage down the long stairway. I breakfast at the café and watch the fishermen unload their catch. And then I board the small boat that is waiting there. Antiparos, they say, do not go there. Antiparos, there is nothing there. I sit on the deck in the light that is like a benediction. I gaze into the blue doorway of the sea. Antiparos. Antiparos. I watch it slowly fade from view.

Counting Cats

I move away from the port to a small village named Kamini. I find a room in a pension with a window and a balcony that looks out to sea. It is quiet, the woman assures me. There is a kitchen that all the rooms share but since it is winter you will have it to yourself. I move in a few days later. In the meantime, a Belgian couple has arrived. And four builders. Two are from Poland, one is from Lebanon and the fourth is a Greek. They refer to the Greek as their master. They keep a large bag of dynamite in the kitchen. It is for the rocks, they say.

On the little street below my window are many cats. They wait hopefully for the garbage bins to overflow. Donkeys walk by carrying loads of building materials. Somewhere out of sight a lamb keeps bleating. Two small English children play. Voices call to one another. A white cat is walking on a red tiled roof.

I have asked for a heater for these cool winter nights. But there is no separate electrical meter for my room. It is a problem, the woman tells me. I have been in this country for almost a year and I show her what I paid last month in a larger apartment that also had a heater. I will pay the same, I say. She and her husband begin to argue loudly. The only words I can understand are, The girl is American and doesn't speak Greek. I am far from being a girl but I don't interrupt. It is very expensive, the husband keeps saying. Come back tomorrow morning, the woman finally tells me.

I leave and they go on arguing loudly. The heater in question glows red if I can get the plug to balance in the heater socket. There is no way of pushing it in. It doesn't fit. And most of the time it falls out.

The kitchen gets more crowded each day. Now there are more large plastic bags. One is filled with laundry and one is filled with shoes. Strange wailing music floats down the hallway. I leave a plate of cookies on the table. I pick some bougainvillea and place it in a vase. I feel outnumbered in this pension. I am trying to make my presence more apparent.

Come back tomorrow, my landlady Zoe has told me and so I do. She shepherds me to a house across the road. She is looking for a translator. A Dutch woman named Ingeborg lives there with her husband Mikalis who is Greek. Zoe and I have been understanding one another all along, but I guess this indicates that the forthcoming discussion will be a serious one. Her husband, she says, is insisting that I pay more. I refuse. We each repeat ourselves several times. Our voices grow passionate. And finally Zoe relents.

I stay there awhile and talk to a woman named Sue. We both arrived on this island about a month ago. We complain about the post office where we are not allowed to look at the mail that comes *poste restante*. We don't believe the mail clerk when he says we have no letters. Sometimes we are handed letters for other people whose names bear no resemblance to ours.

Today it is raining. The village clings to a hillside and all the streets descend to the sea. In the rain each street becomes a rushing stream. Each stairway becomes a waterfall. Everyone stands together under the shop awnings watching the rivers of rain. For three years there was no rain on this island. It feels like a holiday.

Below my balcony is the sea. Across the water the hills of the mainland look close enough to swim to. All day the light and mist and shadows flow over the hills. To the west is a large rock shaped like a sleeping woman stretched out on the sea. At night the moon soars behind the clouds with one bright star at its side.

A two day general strike has been called. The government is trying to enact a new law that will put an end to strikes. So as far as I can tell, the strikes are for the right to be able to go on striking. A few months ago the strikes lasted for three weeks. No banks, no telephones and no mail. Tonight as I am leaving the house to go out for dinner, all the electricity goes out. At first we think there has been a power failure. And then we realize it is part of the strike. I walk by flashlight to a café. It is lit with candlelight. And after an hour or two the power is restored.

I find more dynamite in the kitchen. There are two large boxes of it beneath the kitchen table. And above the table is a candle stuck precariously on a bottle. Next to the table is a canister of gas for the stove. I have a Lebanese friend named Joseph on the island. He says I shouldn't be the one to talk to the workmen. They will only tell me it is perfectly safe. But, of course, it is not safe. So each day I have been knocking at Zoe's door. Her husband is there but I have been told it is best not to consult him about anything. Each day Zoe's daughter says, Tomorrow. She will be back tomorrow.

There is a café at the port where everyone gathers in winter. Its tables and chairs are spread out along the sidewalk. It is a good place to read the paper and drink coffee and watch the boats come and go. The cats of the island gather there beside the fishing boats. I like to count them. So far my highest count has been twenty-seven. They sit quietly a foot or so apart. Now and then a fisherman will throw a handful of small fish to them. There is a brief skirmish and the fastest cats come away with a fish.

Yesterday at the café two cats kept jumping up into my lap. I put them down again and again and then gave up. One of them finally jumped up on the table and began lapping from the water glass. The waiter suddenly appeared at my side and flung the glass dramatically into the sea. Why did you do that, he asked me angrily and loudly. But today he is friendly once more. And I can tell by his smile that he enjoyed the show.

I have been on this island for a month now. I am beginning to be accepted. More and more people greet me when I walk by. The baker will not charge me for cookies and sometimes he offers me ouzo. When it rains he asks me sadly if I will leave now. Tomorrow will be better, he promises.

Downstairs there is a Canadian novelist. He sleeps until three in the afternoon. Then he roams the neighborhood insisting that everyone turn off their music. He needs quiet to work. The Belgian man responded by pushing him down the stairs. I had better warn him about the dynamite.

For days now the lamb has been bleating. I go to look for him. He is black and white and very young. He is enclosed in a courtyard with a high wall so I can't touch him. But he quiets at the sound of my voice.

I have dinner with Joseph. He has had many calls from home today. His engagement of two years has been broken. He came to this country to earn money for his marriage and has been working ten or twelve hours each day. But the family of the girl has been asking questions about his past. They learned he used to drink and do bad things. That was all a long time ago and now I have changed, he says. I do not ask questions about her past because I love her and I trust her. But that is all over now, he says. I will never marry. His eyes are dark and sorrowful. It doesn't matter, he says. It is over now. Let's talk of something else.

The weather is stormy. Gray clouds darken the skies and the sea. The wind blows. I go out walking high above the village. Along the way a dog decides to accompany me. A herd of goats hurries by, the young kids running to keep up.

I knock at Zoe's door once more. This time her daughter says she won't be back for a few more days. So I decide to plunge in. I explain about the dynamite and she agrees it should be kept outside. She will talk to her father and she is sure he will insist that the men remove it. When I return home late that night, the dynamite is still there. The candles have burned low. The ashtray on the table is full.

Today the strikes are over. I am awaiting mail and go eagerly to the post office. But they tell me the sea is rough and no boats will come today to bring the mail.

I walk home along the sea. The pile of garbage beside the path has grown huge. Men with donkeys collect the garbage from the hills and bring it here. There is a dump but it is too far for them to go. Every now and then the one truck on the island comes by and collects it. But it has been a long time now and I can smell the spot long before I reach it. Lately even the cats have deserted their posts there. All over the island everyone tosses their sacks of garbage in piles. In a few months a new mayor will take office. He says he will solve the problem. But he doesn't know how.

I run out of typing paper. For days I have wandered the village stopping in each small shop to look for paper. But I have failed in my quest and I am getting frantic. Going to Athens and back takes a day and I don't want to interrupt my work. I remember there is an office where a bookkeeper works. I climb the stairs and plead with the woman there to sell me paper. And I come away happily with three hundred sheets in my hands.

I see Joseph standing alone out on the rocks and fishing. I watch him for awhile casting his line again and again. He has nowhere to cook and gives the fish to his friends. He has told me he is a poet and a musician. I like his quiet gentle manner. But I don't go down to the rocks to speak to him. He looks lost in thought and I don't want to disturb him.

I go to talk to the landlord. He says the dynamite is not dangerous. He says he is willing to risk his house and family. I tell him I have only one life. And he says perhaps I should find another place to stay. Of course I have thought of that. But I am weary of moving. I know these pensions and the thought of a new one fills me with dread. There would be new problems, new dramas. He takes me across the road to Sue and Ingeborg and Mikalis. Mikalis agrees with the landlord that the dynamite is difficult to set off. The women side with me. But the landlord considers the matter settled and leaves. Mikalis goes on assuring me that the dynamite is safe. And then we stand around and chat. As I leave I invite them all to come sometime to have wine on my balcony. Not while there is dynamite in the house, Mikalis tells me with a grin.

I decide all I can do is throw myself at the mercy of the workers. The Lebanese man speaks English. I ask him to please find a place outside for the dynamite because I am afraid. He says he will speak to the master for me and will let me know what he says. I have a sinking feeling that I am going to lose this battle.

It has been a cold stormy day but suddenly the sun breaks through and etches the clouds with light. The offshore rocks seem to be floating in air just above the misty sea. A cat is climbing in the branches of the orange tree.

Late at night there is a knock at my door. It is the Lebanese man and the master. They explain patiently that there is no problem with the dynamite. The Greek has now placed it under his bed so if it blows up he will be the first to die. Somehow that doesn't console me. But it is clear the dynamite stays.

In the morning the sky is blue again. The hills have turned green from the recent rains. The sea is flecked with white and a cool wind blows. From each balcony laundry waves in the wind.

I go down the road to talk to a woman named Elaini. She has a small apartment for rent. She is a friend of Zoe's. I can rent her apartment, she tells me, if I can make Zoe understand my reason for moving. On her table is a vase of narcissi. She has picked them in the mountains. She says they are all in bloom now. Perhaps in a few days we will hike there together.

But when I leave Elaini's I see the writer. He comes to his window to chat with me. He is sad to hear that I am leaving. He asks me to reconsider. The dynamite cannot be set off easily, he tells me. And he wants me to keep on being a part of the household.

I go upstairs and the man from Poland greets me. He is busy sweeping the kitchen floor. He has placed a dish of cookies on the table. I am beginning to feel that I am part of a family. I am beginning to feel like a deserter.

Tonight there is a showing of the second half of *Fanny and Alexander* at the port. I have been told it will be dubbed in English with Greek subtitles. But when it begins, I find it is not dubbed. I watch the lovely photography and try to understand the subtitles. I can only catch a few words here and there. But after awhile I forget that there is anything missing. Perhaps because I have been in Greece so long, I've gotten accustomed to letting the language sweep by me. It allows me to go on with my dreaming.

I think about the dynamite and realize that it is a subject that makes us all smile. The Greeks love the arguments and the drama. So do the neighbors. The landlord greeted me today with a cheery voice. Is everything all right, he asked me. I don't know, I responded gruffly. Yes the dynamite is safe and everything is fine, he told me happily. The mood is infectious. We are all waiting to see what happens next.

And what happens next is that I look around at my lovely room. A double bed and a thick white quilt with blue hearts. A small table with a white tablecloth and a vase filled with flowers. Even a bookcase and a desk. And a balcony where I have my breakfast on sunny days. At night I sit outside wrapped in a blanket watching the Milky Way spill across the sky. Perhaps I will stay.

I wonder what I can say to Elaini to make her understand my change of mind. Lately I always seem to be embarrassed at myself. It is morning and I walk to the bakery. I have decided I will bring her some baklava. The sun is warm today. Ducks waddle beside me along the path. Cats follow behind me. Donkeys stand beside the road waiting to be saddled. Music pours out from the windows. The baker wraps the baklava in gold paper and ties a bright ribbon around it. And then I go to see Elaini. She greets me warmly. She seems unperturbed by my change of heart. We drink Greek coffee together and part as friends.

I go back and sit on my balcony and take a deep breath. The sea is motionless. Sparrows dart in and out of the eaves. A flock of black and yellow birds lands in the orange tree. The wind is sweeping dark shadows across the water as if vast schools of fish were gliding by.

Later in the day I hear strange voices in the hallway. Two new men are being shown the room across from mine. I stand in the doorway with a sinking heart. Zoe assures me they are staying for only one night but when I go into the kitchen I see that the refrigerator is filled with their food. The house rings with voices and radios playing and doors opening and closing.

I shut myself in my room and play solitaire. I am soothed by the patterns the cards make. They are impersonal. They are random. Sometimes none of the cards will fall into place. But if I am patient, now and then there is a sudden harmony.

I go walking high up on the mountain. There are pine forests and grassy meadows. The earth has been recently tilled and the color is so rich and brown that I wish I had brought paints and a sketch-book. I walk up and up until my legs ache. My ankles wobble on the long walk home.

I count the cats today. When I reach thirty-five, someone tosses them some small fish and they go scrambling after them. I was almost finished counting anyway.

When I reach home, I gather up my towels and sheets and pillow-cases and take them down to Zoe. She and her husband and her daughter and her mother are sitting at the table. They all smile when they see me. I have come for clean sheets and that means I am staying. Zoe goes into the back of the house and returns with clean linens for me. They offer me a cup of coffee and I visit with them for awhile. And then I climb back up to my room.

Offering

On the stone wall opposite my balcony, a kitten is playing with its shadow. A shepherd calls from the rocky hillside. A southern wind is blowing. Rocks gleam beneath the sea.

My landlady Katerina rides her donkey each week to a village four or five kilometers away. There is a good well there and she carries back the drinking water for her family. She sits astride her donkey, holding a portable telephone in her hand.

I've been living on this island all winter, huddling beside my heater in the evenings, bundling up in warm clothes in the afternoons to take long walks up the rocky hillsides. I had been living on an island further from the mainland and stopped here for a weekend on my way home. I am still on my way home. But slowly. *Segá, Segá,* the Greeks say.

Now it is early spring and there is a fragile warmth to the days. I walk the path that winds above the sea to a tiny village a few kilometers away. The fields are covered with flowers that seem to have sprung up overnight . . . white daisies, anemones, forget-me-nots. Even the bright orange poppies are beginning to unfold. I pass a long procession of caterpillars, each one touching the next. Their nests are in the pine trees, white gauzy balls. They kill the trees and are poisonous to the touch. *Kámbia,* they are called, and the word always evokes a shudder from the islanders. Here and there along the road I pass a group of them curled up together in a tight ball.

In the afternoon I have coffee at the café with Pantelis. He complains that his whole body itches because when he was walking in the mountains the caterpillars fell down on him. And he tells me about a millipede as long as a snake that is highly poisonous. It can kill children, he says, or cause an adult to have a heart attack.

I first met Pantelis in the port a few months ago, a rugged handsome man who drives one of the two trucks permitted on the island. All other vehicles are forbidden, even bicycles. For transportation there are a few water taxis and burros that can be hired. But for the most part everyone walks.

Pantelis drives the garbage truck. This gives him the opportunity to wave and chat with everyone along the narrow road. He has a wife and children and though he talks about them, I know I will never meet them. Their place is at home, not in the bustling harbor where boats come and go and donkeys stand patiently waiting. Not at these sunlit cafés along the sea where the travelers gather and where Pantelis loves to sit and drink and talk. That first day we talked about the wild narcissi that grow in the mountains. He knows where they grow and says he will take me there in the truck. We agree to meet in the afternoon.

I mention to one of the foreign women living here that I am going to the mountains with Pantelis. She warns me against it. I consider her warning and decide to trust my own instincts. When he picks me up there is also an old man in the truck. He smiles at me but doesn't seem to want to speak. Before we begin our climb into the hills, we come to a huge chasm in the road. The truck halts and Pantelis seems undisturbed. Laborers are working there and after awhile the gaping hole has been filled with rocks and dirt and we are on our way. We climb the winding dirt road and then Pantelis stops the truck and climbs out. He springs up the bank to show me a few of the flowers which are almost perfectly camouflaged against the prickly shrubs. He climbs back into the truck saying he will return for me in a little while. I scramble over the hillside, pleased to find a few delicate flowers here and there. The old man climbs in another direction and is soon out of sight. After about an hour Pantelis returns and we climb back into the truck. The old man holds a huge bouquet of flowers and presents them to me with a shy smile. I hold the flowers happily and their sweet scent fills the truck as we bump home along the dusty road.

And it is at the port that I first see Elaini. A cool breeze is blowing and the brightly colored boats sway on the blue sea. John and Joanna, two Americans living on the island, have told me about this little ten-year-old. I look up and see her frail crooked body, her tilted smile. Her face is full of brightness. They have just bought red sneakers for her and she holds up each foot proudly to show me. This is the first time she has been to the port and she runs about excitedly. She is said to be deaf but no one is certain of this for she has never been tested. I have the feeling she is hearing me rather than reading my lips. She cannot speak and yet she gives strange halting cries.

I take her to a toy store that day and buy her a large stuffed bear. I hold it out to her regretting that my Greek is too limited to tell her she can choose whatever animal she wants. And then when I see her face I know it doesn't matter. She is hugging the bear against her thin chest and giving happy bird cries.

Elaini lives with her mother at the top of the village. Beyond her house are only the footpaths that continue to wind up the mountain to the isolated monasteries. Once I went walking there. On the rooftop of the house two large dogs barked and lunged at me until their chains choked them. Elaini's mother was outside and I told her I was afraid of the dogs. She screamed at me in rapid high-pitched Greek and continued her screaming long after I was out of sight.

Now John and Joanna are renting the neighboring house. They befriended Elaini gradually and now she visits whenever her mother allows her to. They have slowly expanded their care, making certain not to offend the mother. Joanna gives her baths and brushes out her fine hair. They feed her nourishing food. They have bought her warm clothing but all their gifts seem to disappear once she returns home.

I have heard the Greeks are ashamed of their deformed and hide them away at home. When John and Joanna first met Elaini, she had been dirty and neglected, her hair tangled and matted. I have seen her crayoned drawings, the colors dark and every chimney and pathway shaped like a penis. The anatomy is carefully delineated. Elaini has no father but her mother's boyfriend often stays at the house.

As I walk around the village with Elaini, I ask the villagers, Do you know this girl. Yes, they answer, Yes we know Elaini. I don't know what answer I had hoped for. John and Joanna and I have talked about Elaini and how we could help her. We thought perhaps if the villagers became more aware of her, they might want to improve her life. And yet they seem to know her and be unconcerned.

John and Joanna are ready to take Elaini home and so I hug her and watch her frail body moving away still clasping her bear. She turns back to wave before they disappear around the bend. I wander away from the port and climb out on some rocks next to the sea. At my feet the waves splash in gently. I sit and look out at the misty hills of the Peloponnese. Somewhere nearby a donkey brays. I have been told that when a donkey here grows too old, its legs are tied together and it is tossed from the mountaintop.

In the morning I climb the hills and gather a few spring flowers to bring back to my room. I find a strange succulent with a flower that is two shades of pale green. I pick one and the stem pours a milky sap on my hands. At home I wash my hands with care. And then I put in contact lenses. The burning sensation is immediate and intense. I have the contacts out again in only a few seconds. But my eyes go on painfully burning and I don't know what to do.

I run across the road to my neighbors, a Greek man and his Dutch wife. Both speak English well. They listen to my story and call the poison center in Athens. The man there suggests I wash my eyes in water. They try to reach the island doctor but he isn't in. I rinse my eyes continuously but the pain doesn't lessen. I wash them in chamomile tea, known for its soothing properties. I hold my head under the water tap and submerge my face in a basin of water. But the pain seems to increase and I am frightened I will go blind. Everyone is kind but no one knows what to do.

It is night when we finally reach the doctor. He refuses to see me but instructs me to go to the pharmacist, to wake him if necessary and get a certain ointment. A woman takes me there leading me by the hand up endless stairways and through the narrow lanes. The pharmacist is asleep but he comes down from his room to prepare the ointment for me and put it in my eyes. It takes only a few moments for the pain to ease.

My eyes are tired and aching for days but I am grateful that my vision is normal. I take sweets to the pharmacist and bring a bottle of wine to my friends. And weeks later I will come to a passage about the plant in a book. It is called spurge:

> . . . The hillsides glow with the vivid green and yellow of
> spurge bushes. Local people say it is poisonous and that for-
> merly it was used by fishermen to drug the fish before
> catching them.

I sit on a bench in a small grassy plaza. About a dozen cats are sleeping here and there in the warm sunshine. The tangerine trees are bright with fruit. Windfall tangerines are strewn over the stones like bright jewels. This island whose beauty makes my heart sing. This island that sears me.

The days move past, some cool and cloudy, some with a feel of spring. Wherever I walk I look for Elaini. At last I see Joanna at the post office and she invites me to an afternoon tea at her house. We sit out on the veranda, high above the harbor. And for a moment Elaini appears, running toward me with her arms held out. But she never reaches me. Joanna means well when she stops Elaini and asks where her bear is. And I have a premonition of what will happen next. She turns and runs back to her house to fetch the bear. The door is shut loudly behind her and she does not return.

We go on talking about her. She has never attended school but John has arranged for her to be in an art class. Our hope is that the teacher may somehow be able to help. And there is talk of social welfare agencies. We know of one in Athens. But if she were taken from her mother and put in an institution her life could be far bleaker. Anything we think of could have a terrible backlash. Even our friendship with her is fraught with darkness for all of us will be leaving. There is a French woman present who is a nurse. She has been quietly listening. Now she tells us she believes that Elaini has neurological problems and that she will die soon. She says on a small island like this a deformed child is not allowed to live long. The family somehow sees to that.

It is a few mornings later and I sip coffee at a café at the port and offer the small containers of cream to the hungry cats. A crane lifts dirt. Boats come and go and the harbor slowly fills with crowds of people. Pantelis rumbles by in his garbage truck and stops to join me for a coffee. He invites me to go on an overnight trip with him to the mainland. This has happened before so he knows what my answer will be. He speaks little English but he cries out forlornly, Why. Why you won't go with me. I have tried to answer his question before. I have said that he has a wife and children but that answer doesn't do. I search around in my small Greek vocabulary for an explanation. And suddenly I realize the word idealist has Greek roots. *Ime idealistíki,* I try hopefully. Pantelis laughs and shrugs his shoulders in surrender. And we turn to watch the well-dressed crowds of people still arriving. Tomorrow is Carnival and many Athenians have come for the holiday. There is to be a big parade.

I rise early and walk the path along the sea to the port for breakfast. The cafés are known by the color of their chairs. The café of blue chairs catches the first sunlight and I sit there and linger over coffee and fresh baked bread. As the morning continues more and more people fill the little port. They are wearing elaborate costumes. The parade begins to slowly form.

People begin walking and I fall in behind the others. We wind our way through the narrow streets. A small band plays music. We walk a few kilometers along the sea wall, past chapels and whitewashed houses and stairways to the blue sea. The hills are scattered with bright wildflowers and a flock of sheep are grazing there. At last we reach a little port. A traverna has opened its doors and set out tables with food and retsina for everyone. There is music and a wide circle of dancers. At the center an old man spreads his arms out wide and turns with a quiet dignity. There are many children and families and old people, perhaps a few hundred people in all.

After an hour or so the procession begins anew. This time it winds up and up through the winding paths. Our next destination is a whitewashed square named *Kala Pigadia,* Good Wells. There are two deep wells here and the villagers come each day with their donkeys and jugs to fetch drinking water. A cool wind is blowing but nobody seems to mind. There is more wine and food, more music and dancing. Sunlight streams into the square. Behind us the mountains rise steeply into the cloudless blue sky.

I realize that the time has finally come for me to leave the island. I follow the others up and up for another few kilometers. We stop at last high up in the hills. A long table with wine and bowls of olives is set beside the narrow road. I sit on a stone wall and gaze down at the breathtaking view of the sea far below. In a field just below me a donkey lifts its head and gives a hoarse unearthly cry.

I remain there sitting on the wall as the parade slowly winds its way back down to the port. Soon I am alone there in the wind and the silence. And my thoughts fly to Elaini, this child who is a stranger, this child who is a part of me. I want to take her with me when I board the ferryboat. I want to gather her up in my arms and hold her until she heals. Of what use to her are prayers or tears or hopeless love. And yet I offer them.

House in the Olive Grove

The small house I have rented is still not ready. I wrote to Yiorgos, my landlord, when it was still winter and he assured me that everything had been done. But all the furniture is wet and sticky with shellac. I place my desk outside in the wind to dry but it is still as wet as before. The house is in need of whitewash inside and out but there was no time, Yiorgos explains.

There is a large pile of cement in the courtyard and today Yiorgos brings Manolis, an old man with a lined and beautiful face who works for him. The aim is to use up the cement. And so they extend the patio, leaving large olive oil tins half buried in the wet cement. I ask about them and Yiorgos laughs. Don't you think they are beautiful, he asks me. And then he explains that in a day or two they will remove them, leaving a square of dirt for a tree or a plant. It is close to a hundred degrees outside and they work all afternoon beneath the relentless sun. I have a blue hat with a wide brim that I hand to Manolis. He smiles and sets it over his cap.

They have brought lunch with them and they invite me to picnic with them beneath the olive trees. There is marinated fish and crusty bread and cucumbers. We laugh and talk, half in English and half in Greek. And we make many plans. They will whitewash the house. Yiorgos will bring me two canaries in a cage to place beneath the trees. There is a pool that is used to irrigate the garden and he will clean it and fill it with fresh water for me to swim in. In the back of the kitchen is a pile of old mattresses and bed frames and tomorrow he will come take them away. But time moves slowly in this country. It has been many days since I requested a second set of sheets. When I ask about them I am told his mother-in-law must first buy some material and then they must be cut and sewn. I will bring them later, Yiorgos tells me.

I have been given many warnings. First there is the problem of my neighbor. He is a bad man, a Turk, and I shouldn't talk to him. And then there are the snakes. It is May and the season when the snakes mate. They are especially aggressive at this time. At night it is important to carry a flashlight and a forked stick to hold down the head of any snake that might block my way and to also carry a knife in case I am bitten. There are scorpions whose bite is very painful. And there are the Albanians. Many of them have moved to the island in the last few years so I should be sure to always lock my door. I've never locked my doors nor been afraid in this country. The warnings seem excessive.

Yiorgos helps me with my Greek and sometimes asks me questions about English. Today he wants to know about the pronunciation of the letter *o*. He doesn't understand why it can be pronounced in so many different ways. His voice grows querulous. This is something I've never thought about before and I make up a list of words, certain that I can come up with a rule to help him: shovel, book, long, moon, stop, shore. But I find that I can be of no help at all. That same querulous note has accompanied many of my questions about Greek. I am consoled somehow whenever I realize that English too has its difficulties.

My house is filled with things and most of them are dusty. There are trunks filled with old clothes that smell of mold. Each shelf is covered with pottery. Yiorgos is a diver and there is a large locked cabinet containing careful arrangements of shells of every sort. Tables too are adorned with shells and with coral. The furniture is dark and massive and abundant. In the front room there is a double bed with old silver railings, two sofas, some end tables, a trunk, a desk, a heavy cabinet and a dining table and four chairs. On the floor are old faded carpets. On the walls hang pages from calendars picturing Greek islands and another set that shows parks in the United States. A bare light bulb hangs from the ceiling, encircled by old-fashioned keys dangling from a rusty circle of tin.

I had seen the house briefly two years before. I was drawn by the privacy and the garden and the silver-gray olive trees. It had a fireplace which meant it could be warm in the winter. Indoor heating of any kind is a rarity here. Yiorgos was planning to fix it up for a rental. And we talked of my coming sometime to be its first tenant. Two years went by and an occasional exchange of letters. And finally I wrote to say I would be returning to Greece and would rent the house. Yiorgos met me at the ferry late one night and brought me here. I was too tired to think clearly. I did have the presence of mind to try the bed. It was just what I feared . . . musty and lumpy and hard as stone. I explained politely that I couldn't sleep there. Yiorgos seemed to understand. Or perhaps he merely feared that I would leave. Early the next morning he brought a newly purchased mattress for me.

A lizard comes to drink from a tiny puddle beneath the outside water faucet. A few crimson poppies balance on thin stems. At night something chirps again and again in a high-pitched voice.

I wander down to the beach to have dinner. Small cafés stretch out along the sand. Each has a canopy of bamboo to provide shade. It is

too early in the season for many travelers. The thin beach cats sit
patiently, hoping for a handout. Two ducks are gobbling up bread
someone has tossed to them. I have dinner and then go on sitting
there watching the sea washing into shore and the twilight falling
everywhere. And then I walk slowly home. A brown and white dog
accompanies me. He leads the way and I like to think he is protecting
me from snakes.

The next afternoon Yiorgos comes to work in the garden. He talks
about a beautiful piece of land that Manolis owns in the mountains.
We will all walk there together one day, he promises. And then he
tells me that Manolis has a few donkeys who are getting old. Soon
he will take them to the top of the mountain and push them off. I
have heard of this practice before on another island. I didn't know
it also happened here. I ask Yiorgos if I can keep the donkeys in the
olive grove. He agrees that there would be plenty of weeds and grass
for them to eat. But, he says, they would have to wear something to
keep their heads down to protect the trees. And they would have to
be hobbled. And finally he says that Manolis would never agree to
that. I look up the word for cruel in my dictionary. *Skiliós*. It is very
cruel, I tell him. He smiles and agrees. Yes, it is cruel.

It is evening and grape vines sway in the breeze. The sun-baked
earth grows cool. Outside the garden wall a herd of goats hurries by
with their bells clanging.

I sit in Kostos' café. We have been friends for years. He tells me that
yesterday morning there was an earthquake, *énas seismós*. It was deep
in the sea near Crete. I sit with Kostos, his mother Maria and some
friends who have a little minimarket next door. Kostos serves us
ouzo and fish, fried potatoes and salad. The only business all day
at the café were some children buying ice cream, they tell me. I sit
listening to the music of their voices, understanding little. Kostos
translates for me now and then. They speak of other earthquakes, a

huge one in Athens years ago. And of ghosts. Manolis tells a long story about ghosts in a house in Germany that he once lived in. The others laugh and scoff and say they don't believe it.

I notice a white glow that illuminates the crest of the mountain. And then a huge full moon slowly rises. It seems to sit motionless on the peak. And finally it lifts slowly over the sea. I walk home and climb the white stairway to my roof. And then I sit looking out across the olive groves to the sea beyond. Moonlight falls everywhere and crickets sing.

I am attempting a truce with the dog across the road, a large german shepherd guard dog behind an iron fence. Each time I walk by, it barks loudly and fiercely. The problem seems to be that I startle it. So now whenever I approach I sing a Greek song. And the dog rarely barks at me.

The days and nights flow by and I see little of Yiorgos. He makes a few more promises but the house remains unchanged. He does bring me a bedside lamp at my request. That night I turn it on and after a few moments the bulb shatters and glass falls everywhere. I decide to travel to other islands for a few weeks. It is still easy to find rooms since the high season hasn't begun. And I have a vague hope that perhaps when I return the house will be ready at last.

It is late afternoon when I finally return. I take a bus from the port to my village. Then I carry my bags down the dusty road to the house. The dog barks loudly despite my singing. I guess we will have to form our pact anew. And I find that the gate is locked. Yiorgos and I talked just before I left and he agreed that he would not lock it since I had no key. I wearily toss my bags over the fence and prepare to walk back to the village to telephone him. And then I realize his number is in one of the bags that is now lying on the ground on the far side of the high metal fence. I search around on the side of the road until I find a long stick. And then I catch the handle of the bag that contains his number and drag it under the rails of the gate.

I telephone Yiorgos from Kostos' café. He is away but his wife Katarina promises to come with the key. Since she lives far away and has no car, I settle down for a long wait. I tell Kostos about my travel adventures. And then I have dinner. It is late at night when Katarina arrives with the key. Her father has driven her here. She leaves and it is time once again to walk back down the road past the dog that is barking fiercely and to unlock the gate.

I am happy to find that the outside of the house has been white-washed. But inside everything is the same. The beds are still piled up in the corner of the kitchen. I open all the windows and the shutters to the cool night air. I unpack slowly. I light a few candles and turn out the bare bulb that glares overhead. And then I make a cup of tea and carry it to a small table in the garden. I want to sit beneath the olive trees for a few moments before I sleep. A gust of wind suddenly slams the door shut. I run to open it, knowing already that the situation is hopeless. It can only be opened with a key. And the key is inside.

A cool wind has begun blowing steadily, and I stand there in my thin dress, unable to believe what has happened. I walk from window to window. Each one has strong metal bars. I try the door again and again. I gaze inside where the candles are glowing warmly and my bed awaits me. But I am outside and the night is dark and moonless and cold.

I feel my way along the rough road toward the lights of the village. Kostos' café is dark now and shuttered. So are the others that I try. I think about buses or taxis but it is much too late and I have no money and don't know where Katarina lives. At the end of the road

I find a little taverna that is still open. A fisherman named Stellios is there. I explain what has happened and ask if he will try to telephone Katarina for me. Once again the number is behind a locked door. He and some others try half-heartedly to find the number in the telephone book. But they quickly give up. It is almost one o'clock, they tell me. It is too late to telephone. You will find Katarina at the school tomorrow where she teaches, they say. And finally I have to admit that they are right. *Ékeis díkeo,* I tell them. *Ékeis díkeo.* You are right. They look relieved. Everyone is ready to go home and the taverna owner begins to turn off the lights.

Stellios rents rooms and he offers me one for the night. They aren't ready yet, he tells me, but you will be all right for the night. He takes me there and opens the door. There are two beds. On top of one of them are the plastic tables and chairs from the balcony. An open refrigerator sits in the middle of the room. I quickly and gratefully accept. He goes off and finds sheets and a blanket, a towel and even a roll of toilet paper for me. We smoke a cigarette together and every now and then he shakes his head and laughs. He realizes I have no money to take a bus tomorrow to find Katarina and gives me a thousand drachma note. And finally he wishes me goodnight and leaves.

It was years ago that I learned that the plans we weave with such certainty are as fragile as a dream. I learned that whatever we cling to and claim as our own can vanish into air. I thought I would never forget. And yet I feel fragile and startled in this unfamiliar room. I finally make up the bed and climb wearily into it. I sleep and wake and sleep again. I dream of emptiness, of candles flickering in silent rooms.

It is early when I wake. I dress and leave. I have no pockets so I carry my thousand drachma note in my hand. The cafés are not open yet and I know that Katarina will be teaching until noon. I walk down the road to the house. I want to be sure the candles have burned themselves out safely. I want to try the door once more. But most of all I want to sit in the garden which seems like a haven. As I enter the gate, I pause. A white heron stands beside the pool. Birds are not abundant in this country and this one is a rare visitor. It casts a dream-like spell over the pool and the garden and the bright still morning.

When I leave an hour or two later, the bird is still there. I walk back to the village. I go to have a coffee at Kostos' café. He and another friend, Athanasios, will laugh when they hear of my strange plight. Athanasios has just arrived on the island to work in the café. He tells me he wants his life to become simple. Ninety words, he tells me. Ninety words is all that one needs. And ever since he said it, I have been musing over what my ninety words might be. He tells me he has dreams of traveling to Iceland, to Russia and to America. On his first day he met a woman from Iceland, on the second he met a man from Russia. And on his third day he met me.

We set off together to the main village to look for Katarina. I have been treated to coffee and breakfast and bus fare, and I still hold my drachma note in my hand. I show Athanasios and he smiles. Simplicity, he says. We climb the footpath toward the school and stop to ask directions. A woman tells us that it is a school holiday. Katarina, she says, is on the beach that we have just come from. And so we have one more coffee and board a bus to go back. A radio plays loud jaunty music and the wind blows in through the open windows. We speed along the winding mountain roads back to the beach. And there we spot a large group of children playing. Katarina is nearby. I explain what has happened. She tells me there is no other key. Yiorgos is in Athens until tomorrow, she says cheerfully. There is nothing to be done.

Athanasios and I set off to the house. He is certain he can find a way to get in. And he wants to see the heron. We find it in the same spot where I left it, posed on slender graceful legs. We check each door and window but there is nothing we can do. And then I notice my small purse lying on the sofa beneath the window. The window is open and barred. A flimsy screen is attached with thumbtacks to the frame. It is a simple matter to lift up a corner and catch the strings of my purse and draw it out.

And yet I feel an odd reluctance to have it back. Inside there are many things—money and a small flashlight, a hairbrush, a pen and a small pad of paper. They feel strange in my hands.

Athanasios must hurry back to work at the café. And I go to find Stellios and return his money that is still untouched. He agrees to rent me the room for another night. I go to the store and buy a toothbrush and a bottle of shampoo, still feeling that strange resistance. I return to the room and take a long shower. I brush my teeth and brush my hair. And I wonder at the sense of loss that drifts through me.

The hours pass slowly. It feels peaceful not to have my usual heavy bag of books on my shoulder . . . always a novel or two and a journal and one or two Greek grammar books. I've been trying for years to learn this language. It has been a slow unfolding. Lately I listen to the Greeks when they speak English. It seems to teach me more about the structure of their language than all the carefully organized lessons in my books. A stream of words flows through me. Even in my sleep, in my dreams, it continues. Learning is awkward. It is humbling. Yet every now and then a sentence seems to flow out effortlessly. I think about the word surrender. I take out my notepad and pen and write it down. It is the first word on my list.

Once again I walk back to the house. I sit in the shade of the olive trees. I watch the heron and bathe in its silent beauty. I fill the watering can and water the parrot trees and the roses, the hibiscus and the yellow flowers that open their petals at night. I fill the can again and again.

Tiredness washes over me. I feel like I haven't slept soundly in a long time. Perhaps sleep will be on my list of ninety words. Sleep and wind and sea. The clouds begin moving in and a cold wind begins to blow. I have no sweater so I decide to go back to my rented room. In the middle of the road are two pale green snakes. They are wound together in a tight intricate knot.

Even though it is hardly evening, I double my blanket and climb beneath it. I hear an odd persistent sound and look outside. It is raining lightly. In only a few minutes it builds to a steady downpour. Thunder roars overhead. I watch water slowly seep beneath the door and spread out across the floor.

I think briefly about food. I haven't eaten since morning. But it is much too cold and wet to go out in only a light dress. It seems simpler to go to sleep. I lie there in the gathering darkness and listen to the thunder and the pounding rain. After awhile the rain begins to lessen. And for a few moments music floats through the air from some nearby taverna, an aching harmony of joy and sorrow. And then I sleep.

The next morning Yiorgos returns and gives me a key to the house. The sky is blue and sunlight falls everywhere. I find the white heron lying dead beneath the trees. A white feather drifts in the breeze.

EARLY SUMMER

The wind in summer travels across the sea from Africa. It is a warm wind that carries moisture. Its touch is a caress, stirring my hair and whispering against my skin. The silvery olive branches shimmer and sway in its embrace. Here it is called the Sorokos and when it blows the flowers dance gently on their fragile stems. But there is another wind, a north wind that blows wildly, slamming doors and windows, chasing dust through the air. It blows for days at a time in wild erratic gusts. After awhile everyone is confused and disoriented, like voyagers on a wildly pitching ship.

Today there is only a warm breeze. I sit in the garden beneath the trees, sipping coffee. A new morning glory vine has begun to climb a string and I am waiting for its first blooms. The jasmine has begun to flower. Its sweet aroma drifts in the air. Geraniums and pink oleander line the stone walls. Today the hibiscus has six flowers. They will bloom for only a day, their bright orange petals flung open to the sky. At twilight they will die, as gracefully as they have lived. Their petals close again like a bud. And sometime in the night they will fall soundlessly to the earth.

Beyond the high wall surrounding my house is a narrow dirt road. Now and then a car or a motorbike goes by leaving a cloud of dust in the air. In the evening the shepherd passes by with his dog and his flock of goats. The old women of the village come on foot in the late afternoon and climb the long white stairway to the chapel on the hill. And in the dirt of the road are huge curved footprints of the bulls.

From where I sit in my garden, I can see the bulls in the field across the road. They first appeared a few days ago. They are so large and motionless that they are almost invisible. They look like huge black shadows beneath the olive trees. It is only when their long black tails sway from side to side that they take form. *Távri,* they are called, these huge bulls with long curving horns.

My hours are becoming more like my Greek countrymen. It was about three in the morning when I walked home along the dirt road. I looked for the bulls in the moonlight but they were gone. And sometime during the morning while I still slept, I heard something, enough to sense that if I jumped up and ran to the gate, I would see the bulls being led along the narrow road. But my sleep was sweet and instead I fell back into a sea of dreams. When I finally woke in the late morning, the bulls were back.

It is the passage of the bulls that concerns me. I can walk past their field with hardly a tremor. But when the field is empty I wonder if I will encounter them around the next bend in the road. The road is narrow and lined with thick thorn bushes and there would be nowhere to retreat. Stellios lives down the road, and in my limited Greek I ask him if the bulls are okay. I don't know, he laughs, and throws up his hands. *Fovoúmai légo,* I am a little afraid, I tell him. He instructs me, Don't wear red and don't smoke. Why shouldn't I smoke, I ask. He laughs again and says, Because the end of the cigarette would be red.

You have a fear of fear, a woman told me many years ago. Her words were wise. I look at the hibiscus flowers swaying in the breeze and the bulls across the road grazing contentedly beneath the trees. And I look at my fear, at its emptiness, and watch it fade away.

I gather up some paints and brushes and a sketchpad and put them in a bag. I fill a small jar with water. I don't know how to paint but in this country I often find myself trying. It is a longing to recreate the beauty that surrounds me, a longing to pay homage to it. I wander down the dirt road and find a footpath that winds up and up to a white chapel in the mountains. And there I sit on a wall and spread out my supplies. I want to paint what I see before me, the pale earth-colored hills, the thorn bushes and olive trees and in the distance that unforgettable blaze of blue that is the sea. I lose myself in the colors and shapes. But what appears on my page doesn't seem right. I put color over color to try to capture the soft brown of the hills, the gray and white stones, the silvery tips of the olive trees and the pale untroubled blue of the sky. Only the sea seems to come out right, with brush strokes of every shade of blue I can create, and purple and greens and flecks of white. And then suddenly the wind comes gusting up the mountain and lifts my paint brushes and tosses them into the thorn bushes far below. I can see them lying there in a place that is impossible to reach. I muse about whether this is a judgment of my artistic talent. And then I slowly wind my way back down.

In the evening I walk down to the little village that stretches along the beach. When I arrived here a few months ago there were only a few sleepy cafés, a few travelers, and some hungry beach cats. Now each morning the beach is filled with shouting children and swimmers who arrive on crowded buses from the main village. People play paddle ball and dogs romp and the cafés are filled. By nightfall the beach grows quiet. People gather in the cafés to dine and watch the sea that gleams in the moonlight. Music floats through the air.

I walk along the beach uncertain which café to choose. And then I see an older Greek woman named Anna that I met a few days ago. We talked a little, sometimes in Greek, but mostly in English. Unlike my Greek, her English is very good. Anna is sitting alone and I ask if I may join her. She seems pleased to have company. We eat and sip wine and chat together with the uneven rhythm of strangers. I tell her about my painting adventure and she describes how she spent her day. I sometimes have a problem with boredom, she admits. And you, you are staying many months. Do you sometimes get bored.

And though I have certainly known boredom, I don't feel it here. Sometimes I think I would almost welcome it. To illustrate I tell her about the walk to my house that I make a few times a day. I tell her about the bulls and about the fierce guard dog that lives across the road. In the middle of the road I sometimes find snakes. If it is dark when I reach home, I hesitate before I turn on the lights. There are almost always one or two huge insects on the walls, a spider or a beetle or some large gray or mud-colored strangely tentacled insect that slides away into the shadows like a ghost. On the wall just above my bed there is often a pale lizard or two with bulbous eyes.

Anna is an attentive listener. She lives in one of the hotels that line the paved and lighted road, so she is surprised by my description. Do you have any close neighbors, she asks. Are there lights along your road. And of course there are not. You are very strong, she tells me. Very strong to stay so alone. You have courage, *tháros*. I try to explain that I prefer the privacy and quiet, that we all have a different kind of strength. I ask about her work and she tells me she has retired now but she used to be a lawyer working for the Athenian government. And so, I tell her, you also have strength and courage. When you went to law school, it must have been unusual for a woman and very brave. She smiles in her quiet dignified way.

I walk home in the moonlight. The wind has begun once more, its wild gusts sweeping through the night. The bulls are gone. I notice a long curving line that winds back and forth along the road and ends in the weeds. I wonder hopefully if it could be the tail of the bull brushing the earth as he walks. But it looks like the path of a very large snake. I sing as I pass the guard dog and he watches me in silence. And then I sit in the garden. The night flowers have opened their many colored petals and their scent floats in the air. Small green lizards dart over the dry earth. A gray cat with soft brown eyes appears. He often visits and I like his quiet company. A sea of stars floats overhead. At last I go inside and climb into bed. I lie there listening to the sighing of the wind, feeling its cool breath against my face and my hair.

The next morning the hibiscus has four bright flowers. A few more fragile white jasmines have opened their petals. The bulls are so close by I can see one urinate in a thick steady stream. There is a fire on the mountain creating a cloud of smoke. When the wind gusts, the flames leap into the air. I walk down to the village. Others have spotted the fire and say that people will come soon to put it out. And then I sit in a café eating a breakfast of fresh fruit and thick creamy yogurt. Yannis comes into the café, an old man whose house I rented a few years ago. I invite him to sit with me and have a coffee. He speaks no English so our talk is limited. I ask him how he is, and his eyes grow sad. My wife died, he tells me. It was in the winter. And he points to the black armband he is wearing. I tell him I am sorry and then we sip our coffee in silence.

A lovely young woman from Albania works in the café, washing the ever present pile of dirty dishes. Her dark eyes are lined with kohl and are brimming with passion. When Yannis leaves, she runs to sit with me. Today she asks me where I am from. When she hears that I am an American, she breaks into a stream of broken Greek that I cannot understand. But I can tell she is pleading with me to take her to America. Kostos, who owns the café, comes to sit with us and acts as translator. I slowly learn her story. Because she is Albanian, she has no passport. Her husband is in America, and she believes I have the power to simply take her with me. How much does it cost to go to America, she wants to know. When I write down the number, all the vitality vanishes from her face.

She works in a fever during the high season, the way the Greeks do, sleeping only a few hours each night. She has a job as a housekeeper that begins at seven in the morning. She cleans and cooks and irons all day. And then she works as a dishwasher until the last bus comes at midnight to take her home. Her husband will be coming back in two months from a year in America. And she has a three-year-old child who is with her mother in Albania. She tells me she misses them both terribly. But when her husband returns, they will go home together and be with their child again. Her dark eyes dance at the thought. And with their money, they will build a big house. It will have twelve rooms, enough for her parents and brothers to live with them. There is rapture in her smile as she talks of what their life will be like.

The sea today is whipped by the wind. Waves spill into shore and the water gleams with silver light. I swim and let the waves carry me to shore again and again. And then I walk home caked with salt and eager for a shower. But when I turn on the taps, I find they are dry. Like the wind and the bulls, the water seems to come and go mysteriously. Sometimes there is a stream of water, sometimes a trickle and sometimes none at all. My landlord Yiorgos has explained that the water is regulated during the summer to preserve it. The hotels and pensions have private water supplies. I sometimes think I am the only one affected.

The problem has been going on for weeks so I am prepared. Outside in the sun are two buckets full of water and I step out into the courtyard with my soap and shampoo and towel. When I am covered with suds, I raise the buckets and empty them slowly over my head. The shower is never very warm or strong. I prefer this sun-warmed cascade of water and the sun shining down.

I go up on the roof to check on the fire. The smoke is gone now without a trace and from here I cannot see any damage. I hear a cracking sound and see a large olive branch dangling. The bull is eating the leaves. He raises his head to look at me. And then a young man enters the field. I lose sight of him among the trees but a short while later he emerges leading what clearly are two cows, not bulls, on a rope. They are followed by two calves. One bull follows after them. He has a rope tied from his horn to his front leg and he walks with difficulty. My fear turns to pity as he passes my gate, stops to graze on some weeds and then continues hobbling down the road. I remember to look at his tail. It hangs very close to the ground but doesn't touch it. Perhaps I knew that all along.

I take my sketchpad and paints and my one remaining brush into the garden. I want to try to paint the hibiscus with its shining petals and deep blue centers. The stamen extend into the air and end in tiny circles of red velvet. I have trouble with the dry earth. I work on and on, adding more and more colors until it slowly comes to life. I work quickly because the light is fading and the gleaming petals are beginning to close.

It is twilight when I climb up the cascade of white steps to the chapel above my house. Its name is Fainoroumeni, a place where the Holy Mother has appeared. Perhaps it was a shepherd who saw a vision of her on this spot and thus the chapel was erected. I go inside to light a candle. And then I sit on the terrace watching the sun go down behind the mountains. I surrender to this country, to the wind, the bulls, the sea. I surrender to the dust and the heat and the translucent light, to the language that flows through my dreams. Here every stone has a story to recite and the chapel bells carry news of joy and sorrow. No wonder the gods and goddesses roamed this earth. How could they resist its allure. At night the moon seems almost within reach. The stars cascade down and touch the mountaintops. Even death seems closer, less remote . . . death and the wild sweet song of sorrow that accompanies it.

That night as I am falling asleep I realize I haven't dreamed for a long time. I feel unknown to myself, somehow changed by the mysterious spell this island has woven around me.

I wake in the night from a vivid dream. I have been asked to perform a dance. And even though this is something I've never done before, I am unafraid. I decide I will perform the dance in an *alóni*, one of the circular stone threshing floors that abound here. For my costume I will wrap scarves around me. To begin the dance I will recite a small poem in both English and Greek:

Immortality

> There is a red flower
> in my garden
> that blooms
> for a day
> Hour after hour
> beneath the bright dome
> of the sky

Αθανασια

> Υπαρχει ενα κοκκινο λουλουδι
> στον κηπο μου
> που ξει
> για μια μερα
> ωρα μετα την ωρα
> κατω απο τον γαλαξιο τρουλλο
> του ουρανου

As the dance opens I will stretch toward the light. Then I will dance with all the joy and grace and abandon that I can. For an ending I will reach one last time toward the light and then bow my head to the earth.

For many days that follow I linger in the enchantment of the dream. One day while sitting in the wide courtyard of the little chapel above my house, I startle to realize that it makes a perfect stage. It is edged on all sides with a stone bench that could provide the seating. The mountains are the backdrop and, below the courtyard, shimmering olive groves stretch to the sea. And today when I go to the beach a man is selling *kanarínia* or canaries, small clay flutes from the island of Paros. When they are filled with sea water, they make lovely melodic notes. I buy one and sit on the sand playing it. And I imagine the fluting of the *kanarínia* as music for the dance.

Later I sit in Kostos' café and Katarina comes to sit with me. It doesn't matter about a passport, I tell her. You are going to be a queen in Albania. The word queen is unfamiliar to her in Greek. I try to explain but still she doesn't understand. Finally Kostos joins us and manages to convey the meaning to her. She turns to me with her warm irresistible smile.

When I reach home I find that there is water, a rush of water. I take a shower inside to celebrate. And when the sun goes down, I water the garden. I fill the watering can many times. My favorite plants receive a whole sprinkling can of water . . . the hibiscus first and then the red and yellow flowers that perfume the night, the jasmine and the morning glory. I turn on the irrigation system and watch little pools of water forming on the dry earth beneath the geraniums and the roses and then spreading out to the olive trees. I can almost hear the plants and trees sipping thirstily in the heat.

It is warm in the house tonight so I take a pillow and climb up to the roof where a cool breeze blows. I lie there listening to the sounds of the night. Crickets sing and in the distance a lamb bleats. A *koukouváyia,* an owl with a loud chirping voice, calls from a nearby tree. Lizards softly tick. Soft strains of music from the taverna on the mountain float down and distant voices rise and fall. And finally there is only silence and starlight and the night enfolding me in sleep.

LATE SUMMER

I wake to the plaintive bray of a donkey on a nearby hill. I wrap a scarf around me and carry a cup of coffee out into the garden. Even in the shade of the olive trees the heat enfolds me. A hummingbird hovers over a flower. It is as tiny as a thimble.

I turn on the water faucets hopefully. There has been no water for two days. My hopes are quickly dashed. The water is carefully rationed in summer but it has never been turned off for this long. I decide to walk down to a beach café to telephone my landlord Yiorgos. Perhaps he will be able to find out what is going on. I dial his number again and again at the bank where he works. By now I am used to Greek telephones so I am not surprised at all by the strange whistles and squeals, the busy signals and wrong numbers. But after many tries I give up. Then I try to call his wife Katarina. She speaks little English but I think I can communicate what I want. After a few tries, a man finally answers. I ask for her in a hopeful voice. *Den énai Katarina edó,* he says. There is no Katarina here. I am using a telephone in my friend Kostos' café and he notices that I am having trouble. Perhaps the numbers have been changed, he suggests. His own number was changed last week. Is there a way to get the new numbers, I ask with a familiar sinking feeling. No, he responds, and hurries away. It is the peak of the high season and the café is full.

I consider taking a bus to town to find Yiorgos but the heat and the crowded bus make the idea unbearable. I might find a seat on the ride to town but the return trip to the beach would be jammed. I've made the journey many times. At each stop more and more people pile in until we are pressed tightly together. The radio plays jaunty music and the sun beats in as the bus careens around the curves. There is a boy who collects money during the ride, sliding miraculously between the crush of moist bodies as he works his way to the back of the bus. I decide instead to walk back home and think things over. The beach is crowded and noisy with children running and shouting, sunbathers and people playing paddle ball. Music streams into the air from each café, the melodies merging into a blur of sound. I find I am spending more and more time in my garden, sitting at the table beneath the trees.

On the way home I pass an old man who has a small house nearby. I ask him if he has water, and we have a long discussion in Greek. Every now and then there are some words I can understand. He tells me about the meters that regulate the water. And then he says that yesterday he had no water but now he has. This sparks my hope and I thank him and continue home. But I find I still have no water. On an impulse I check behind the house and discover that a lever there is mysteriously closed. When I open it I have water again in plentiful supply. I fill all the containers I have—a plastic wash basin, two buckets and a large watering can. Then I wash a few clothes and a few dishes and head happily back to the beach for a swim.

In the evening Yiorgos shows up. I complain about the water and he shrugs and laughs. And I ask him if his phone numbers have been changed. They are the same, he explains, but because Kostos' number has been changed, it isn't possible to call anywhere on the island from that phone. All I will reach is wrong numbers because the wires haven't been changed yet. It will take a long time, he adds with a grin.

When he leaves I water all the flowers by alternately filling the bucket and the watering can. The hibiscus flowers that opened so brightly all day have already closed their petals and fallen to the earth below. The night flowers cast their sweet scent everywhere. I climb up to the roof and watch the three-quarter moon disappear behind the mountain. It looks like it is toppling from the sky.

157

I go on sitting there in the darkness. A south wind breathes a current of heat through the night. Circadas sing and the Milky Way streams across the sky. Suddenly I hear a loud crash below me. I descend slowly, afraid of what I might find. I look in the living room window and things look undisturbed. But when I go inside and enter the kitchen, I find chaos. The large shelves have fallen off the wall onto the table and floor. There is broken crockery everywhere as well as pots and pans and silverware. The top shelf was a high one and contained baskets I never looked into. So there is a surprise of shells and stones strewn everywhere. A bottle of olive oil has poured its contents out on the floor. I stand looking at it all in wonder. And then I turn off the light and go into the other room. *Áli forá,* I say aloud, another time. And I climb into bed.

Today I take my paints and sketchbook with me to the beach. There is a small white chapel overlooking the sea that I have tried many times to paint. After working at it for hours, I have always torn up each failed attempt. I find a shady wall to sit on and choose a few of the wonderful flat beach stones for my palette. The hillside, with its thorn bushes that I've always found so hard to capture, slowly emerges and this time I am pleased by the way it looks. The sea always comes easily and the pale blue wash of the sky. A fisherman named Stellios walks by and stops to watch. *Oráio,* he says. Beautiful. I want you to give it to me. I am touched that he wants it but I can't part with it. You live here, I tell him. You have all this. But I will be leaving soon. I need the picture to remember. He seems to understand. And I go on painting, adding more and more shades of blue to the sea, as well as tiny dabs of thick white that seem to add light.

A small boy and girl have been sitting beside me, watching. We talk a little though they are shy of my incorrect Greek. When I finally finish the painting, I ask them if they would like to paint. The girl says *ne,* yes, and the little boy says, *Den bouró.* I can't. *Boréis,* I say, *boréis. Énai éfkalo*. You can. It is easy. I give each of them a brush and a sheet of paper and add more dabs of paint to the rocks. The little girl begins at once. First she paints some round beach stones. Then she carefully paints the blue sea surrounding them. There is an artistry to her picture that seems amazing for such a small child. The boy hesitates and then he too begins to paint the sea, adding some dark blurry fish and a boat or two. I tell them both how much I like their pictures. In a little while their parents appear and take them off to lunch.

I walk down to Kostos' café. He pours himself an ouzo and joins me at my table. Was there a small earthquake last night, I ask him, and tell him about my shelves. He says there wasn't an earthquake, but around midnight there was an explosion of dynamite in the mountains, so loud it frightened the people in the café.

Tonight I sit on a quiet part of the beach and wait for the moon to set. It rises above the little chapel at one end of the beach and crosses the sky until it reaches the mountain at the other side. I sit there musing that it would take me only about two hours to walk from where it rises to where it sets.

I walk home along the dirt road in the darkness. I have lived here for about four months and walk this road three or four times a day in each direction. I have picked the wild oregano and oleanders that grow beside it. My feet have learned each rise and depression, the shape of each stone. My footprints are embedded in the soft dust. It seems unimaginable that I am leaving.

In the morning there is water so I decide I will wash my sheets for the last time. My largest container is a bucket and I fill it with soap and cold water and stir the sheets around a bit. Then there is the rinsing. It takes bucket after bucket of water before the suds are finally gone. I wear a bathing suit for I am always as wet as the sheets by the time I am done. I toss the water over the patio so it gets cleaned in the process. The last few bucketfuls, which are almost free of soap, go to the hibiscus and the morning glories. My clothesline is short and I have only five clothespins. So I can hang only one sheet and pillowcase at a time. Then I sit beneath the trees and sip coffee and write a letter as I wait for the sun and wind to dry them. And then I hang out the rest.

There are grapevines in the garden and the grapes have finally grown sweet and ripe. They trail over the ground and their heavy clumps are half hidden by leaves. I gather them, eating as I pick. Then I wash off the dust under the outdoor faucet, tossing away the ones the birds have already tasted. I carry a large bag of them down to the beach to distribute to friends. Kostos and his mother Maria love them and begin eating them immediately. I bring some to Nikos for his restaurant. He tells me that in Greek the tiny grapes are called bells.

At the far end of the beach is a small café run by a family of three generations. I often have dinner there and sit visiting with them long into the evening. Today the grandmother greets me and we talk about the colors of the sea. It is dark purple today at the horizon and then deep turquoise and near the shore it becomes pale blue-green with golden undulating lines. *Polí oráio,* very beautiful, we say. And we talk about the heat which has gone on unabated for days. Will you swim today, I ask and she says yes. I have seen her swimming. Unlike most of her contemporaries who at most will wade out a little way and stand in the water, she swims far out to sea.

Her daughter Foni brings me a *frapé,* a cold whipped coffee, and I sit down at the family table. Manolis, Foni's husband, is in Athens today they tell me. He is a professional musician, a singer and bouzouki player with a sweet smile and a head of unruly white curls. Their daughters Dina and Despina have learned English at

160

school and assist in the conversation. They are hot and weary of the crowds and the nights without sleep. The café often remains open until one or two in the morning. And when it closes Manoli sometimes plays his bouzouki for a few more hours. They all rise early to buy groceries in the central village and fresh fish in another little fishing village. And then they begin cooking for the day. The food in the café is wonderful and they have promised to give me some recipes when I leave.

In the late afternoon I decide to go to the monastery. It is high on the hilltop above my house. I am almost sure there is a footpath that leads up. It is much too hot for the hard climb but I will take the bus there and try to find the footpath to walk home on. It will be downhill all the way. The bus is crammed with people but the ride doesn't take long. And soon I am walking down the long dirt road that leads to the monastery. I find it is locked but there is a wide white courtyard that looks out over the village and the sea below. I sit for a long time entranced by the view. And finally I set off on a little path that heads downward. After ten or fifteen minutes it abruptly ends. I can see the chapel above my house and I can see my rooftop but I cannot get there. I try forging a path amidst thorn bushes and over crumbling stone walls. But soon my legs are scratched and I find myself standing before a high stone wall that seems impossible to climb. I finally accept defeat. I climb up and up back to where I began, hot and discouraged. I reach the monastery and from there the road descends with breathtaking views of the sea.

At home I am pleased to find that there is still water. I shower and toss on some clean clothes. And then I step outside in the twilight. I hear an unfamiliar sound and look up. Forty or fifty very large birds are circling just overhead. Many have landed on the roof. Others are perched on the electric poles. They have long thin bills and their legs are long and slender. They are white except for some black on their wings. There are some children gathered in the road watching them and a man is also gazing up. *Ti énai.* What are they, I call out. *Énai pelargós,* the man replies. And then we all stand watching in silence while the birds circle excitedly, calling to one another and fluttering their long wings.

When it grows dark, I walk down to the beach to Nikos' café. I tell him about the birds and ask him what *pelargós* is in English. He consults his Greek-English dictionary and announces that they are storks. I have to lead him out to the road to show him their silhouettes in the starlight before he believes that they are really here. Storks have never appeared on the island before.

I have dinner at the café and linger on to watch the full moon rise over the mountain. First its light illuminates the mountaintop and then a huge round moon climbs slowly into the sky. *Pansélinos,* it is called. And then I walk down to Manolis' café. Just as I hoped he has returned and is playing the bouzouki and someone has joined him with a guitar. I sit and join the small group of friends gathered there. Someone hands me a tambourine and I play it softly. Tonight the breeze is a little cooler and moonlight gleams on the sea. The music sighs and weeps and floats through the air. It is late at night when I finally walk home. On each electric pole a stork is silhouetted against the moonlit sky.

The house is warm so I climb up to the roof to sleep. I lie there listening to dogs barking and the sharp rising call of an owl. The bright full moon floats overhead now. My hand brushes something soft. A little tiger-striped cat that lives nearby has nestled down beside me. He often visits, lately staying for hours. I feed him milk but he prefers to hunt the small lizards and insects that abound. Most cats in this country are thin and skittish. But this little cat is trusting. It purrs now beneath my hand. This is the first time it has spent the night with me. I can't help wondering if it senses that I am leaving.

At dawn I open my eyes to see if the storks are still here but they have vanished. So has the cat. I go inside and climb into bed to sleep longer. It is a few hours later that I walk down the dirt road for a last breakfast of fruit and yogurt. My friend Yiorgos is there and joins me. You will come back next year, he asks. I will come back, I say, but I don't know when. He has a large garden and asked me a few years ago to send him some tomato and cucumber seeds from an American nursery. I did send him the seeds but though they produced huge plants, the fruit itself was small. Should I try again, I ask him. No, he says, the climate here is too different. We kiss each other gently on both cheeks and say goodbye. I wander here and there along the beach saying goodbye to friends. And I dive into the warm blue sea again and again.

It is late afternoon when I reach home. From my garden I notice a few people climbing the stairs above my house to the chapel. Now I see a priest in black robes climbing the stairs followed by a procession of well-dressed villagers. And I realize there must be a *panayíri* today, a small religious celebration. I check to make sure I am dressed appropriately and climb up after them. I find about forty people gathered in the courtyard. Inside of the chapel the priest is chanting. In the center of the courtyard is a table where the traditional huge round loaves of sweet bread are neatly stacked. On top of them a candleholder has been placed with three tall golden candles. The doorway of the chapel and the walls of the courtyard are festooned with green leafy branches. They are placed carefully between each crack in the white stone walls.

More and more people arrive. I gaze around at the faces. I know so many people here. There is Maria, whose husband runs a little taverna and their two handsome young sons. There is Nikos who works at the post office. And Julius and Moska who run a little pension in the village. Beside them stands their daughter Aspasia.

She was a child the last time I was here, and now she has become a beautiful young girl.

Finally the priest comes out into the courtyard. And an icon is carried out. It is decorated with two tiny bouquets of flowers in the top corners and a careful arrangement of leaves. The huge breads are sliced into thick slabs and passed around in baskets. Cups of strong sweet wine are distributed. It is Nikos who passes around the wine and he makes sure I receive some. People laugh and chat and children run back and forth. I peek into the little chapel. Many candles are brightly burning and each icon is encircled with fresh flowers. Tiny oil lamps are burning with a golden light.

At last the chapel bells begin ringing and people slowly begin to descend the stairs. I linger awhile longer and at last I follow the others down. I walk slowly for I am trying to memorize the soft colors of the olive trees and the graceful curve of the stairway and the sound of the chapel bells that go on and on with their ringing.

House Above the Sea

I

I'll take you in my boat to Vathi, Yiorgos tells me. There is a house for rent there that I have been wanting to see but it is early in the season and there is only one bus a day. The boat is an inflatable raft with many patches but I quickly climb in. Yiorgos insists that I sit on the outside rim. I'd feel safer on the bottom but he tells me the bottom is too weak. I hang onto a frayed rope that looks like it could break at any moment. The wind has picked up and the sea is getting rough. We bounce over the waves and I hold on tightly. *Segá, Segá*, I plead. Go slowly. But Yiorgos only laughs. *Fouvámi*, he asks. Are you afraid. Only a little, I admit. And he can see from my smile that I'm loving the ride.

We pass an uninhabited island with only one tiny chapel. And like all Greek chapels, there is a story to go with it. It was built by fishermen whose boat had been tossed on shore during a storm. In gratitude for finding themselves safe, they wanted to erect a small chapel. They had no water but there was wine in the boat. And so the chapel was built with wine.

And the waves finally cast us gently ashore on a tiny beach in Vathi. Across the bay is the village . . . some white houses with bright blue shutters, a monastery beside the sea, a few tavernas and some rooms

165

to rent. At this side of the bay there is only a pottery and the house of the potter and clinging to the hillside is a small white house. Yiorgos introduces me to Andonis, the potter, and says he'll be back in a little while. Don't forget me, I say in Greek. It's a phrase I know because of forget-me-nots, one of my favorite flowers. Yiorgos laughs and promises to return. The first problem is that we are about to climb a rocky footpath and in the rush of departure I have forgotten my shoes. Andonis shrugs and leads me to a large pair of rubber thongs. And then we go up, much faster than I'd like, with him far in the lead. He unlocks the door to a lovely little house, the sort I've always wanted. All the windows look out to the bright blue sea below. Inside is a room that serves as a kitchen and dining room and sitting room. Next a bedroom with a double bed and a single one. And a bathroom. Many Greek houses are dark but this one is full of light. I ask Andonis how far it would be to walk to the bus and how I would get there. It seems I would have two ways. The first is about a kilometer up a very steep curving dirt road to the top of the hill, and the other would be to walk the beach. I can see the beach and there are places where it is interrupted by rocky outcroppings. I want to ask if there is a way around them but my scanty Greek has run out.

As the island slowly fills with people, the bus schedules are in a state of constant change. A few days later I find there are buses every two hours to Vathi. I go there and manage to find my way back to the little house. It is as lovely as I remember but as I sit on the cement veranda and look out over the view, it seems impossible to live here. I think about carrying my day-pack and bags of groceries and trudging back and forth to the bus. It is about a half hour's walk. The climb up to the main road is impossibly steep. And even the walk along the beach involves a lot of climbing on narrow goat tracks. I grow sad realizing that as I grow older, I may have to let go of some of my impossibly romantic dreams.

I've stayed on this island many times. Now it is June and the villages are still peaceful and timeless. I am renting a room from Yiorgos in a lovely beach village. But the rooms will soon become very expensive and the tourists will soon be arriving and the villages will overflow with people and the buses will be packed. Until a year ago, Vathi had no paved road and no bus. To get there required a two or three hour walk over the mountains on a footpath. I used to come and stay for a few days to soothe my jangled nerves. There was no electricity then, only a generator that would come on for an hour or so in the evening and then there would be only candlelight and starlight and moonlight. There are a few houses I could rent in other villages but this is the only one I can even hope might retain its peacefulness.

My dreams grow vivid during the days and nights of indecision that follow. I dream a woman is dying. I visit her and she seems to have totally accepted her approaching death. I sit and read a book she has written and weep. I dream a Buddhist monk is speaking to me. Watch your fears, he tells me. Look at them and know them and enter them. Watch the way they arise and cease. The next morning I tell Yiorgos I would like to talk to Elefteria, the woman who owns the little house. He tells me she will be coming to the village in a few days and he will try to arrange it. I just want to talk to her, I insist. I have a lot of questions about the house.

A few days go by and suddenly Yiorgos tells me Elefteria will be coming to talk to me in a few moments. She arrives like a whirl-wind, speaking rapid Greek. Yiorgos sits with us to try and act as translator though his English is very limited. I learn there is no hot water but she will arrange to get a hot water heater. She says the house has screens on the windows. I learn that Andonis is her brother. His wife will be coming soon to live below and another family as well. They will help me with rides to the village and to the store. She will come tomorrow afternoon with a taxicab to help me with my luggage. We agree on the rent and she hurries off.

It takes me a few minutes to realize that tomorrow is much too soon for me. I need time to linger over this room, this village where almost everyone seems to be a friend. But Yiorgos explains that Elefteria will be opening a restaurant the day after tomorrow and will be too busy to come after that.

I begin to pack a little and try to compose myself. I drink ouzo with Yiorgos and his wife Maria and we all mourn my departure. I've known them for years and they feel almost like my family. I feel that unease and anticipation return that I felt when I called to buy a one-way ticket to Greece, that sense of vulnerability when everything familiar is being stripped away. All I can do is hope the vision that I have is right. I watch all my fears and doubts and uncertainties and beneath them I can still catch a glimpse of a dream of a house above the sea, a place to read and write and meditate.

The next morning there is work to keep me occupied. Yiorgos will soon open a little bar with take-away food, mostly cold drinks and ice cream. I have talked to him about fruit-shakes and how popular they might be during the hot summer days. And so we have decided to experiment. He removes a new blender from its box and I bring over the leftovers from my little refrigerator—yogurt, melon, bananas and some apricots. He supplies some ice cream and ice. We try different combinations and then he and Maria and I sit at a little table to sample our work. We pronounce them all delicious. I write out *Fruit Shakes* for him so he can make a special sign. And we make a toast to how rich he will become.

In the afternoon I sit with my bags packed and wait for Elefteria. I've said my goodbyes to everyone and promised to come back often to visit. But I wonder how often I will actually come. The bus ride from Vathi to the central village takes a half an hour. Then there is a long wait and another bus ride. Elefteria arrives and we rapidly pile into someone's truck. The driver takes us to the main village and leaves us at the bus stop. When the bus arrives we drag my suitcases inside. And off we go to Vathi. I know that walking the kilometer on a rough dirt road from the bus stop to the house with my luggage would be impossible. Elefteria knows it too and talks to the driver. He uses his pager to try to reach Andonis. He tries again and again and finally gets a response. Elefteria grins at me and sits back contentedly. And indeed Andonis is there in his truck when we get off the bus. We heave the heavy bags up into the back of his truck while he watches us indifferently. And then we drive to the little house.

I've only been inside once before and I look around both eagerly and fearfully. Elefteria is a whirl of action. She pulls out a roll of screen and cuts out window sized pieces. She removes some old ripped screen and thumbtacks new screen neatly in place. She sweeps the linens off the beds and remakes them with clean sheets. She removes armloads of clothes from the closet to put in an over-stuffed trunk in the back room. She clears out the medicine cabinet and somehow manages to find a place to tuck everything away. She works so quickly I can hardly keep track of what she's doing. I think about helping but everything is happening much too rapidly.

While Elefteria is sweeping the floor, I wander around trying out things and asking questions in my awkward Greek. I point out that the toilet doesn't flush. She leads me outside to a small well and lowers a bucket. Then she carries the water inside and pours it in the toilet. No problem, she says, no problem. Andonis will start the water in the toilet. And she tells me again that there will be hot water but the heater seems to be coming from Athens and will take awhile longer.

She shows me how to work the propane burners and asks what else I might need. I sneak a look at the bed. Three thin mattresses are piled on top of one another. I've slept on these beds and they are lumpy and uncomfortable. So as tactfully as I can, I tell her all the rooms for tourists have new mattresses. She promises to get one right away. She can't find the measuring tape but she finds thread and takes measurements with that. I try to open the back door but it won't budge. Elefteria tries too. There is an old key in the door and when she tries to turn it, it breaks in her hand. No problem, she says and turns away. She wipes the tables and counters with care.

Then we sit down together for a few moments. She tells me I shouldn't drink the water. It comes from a cistern and she would worry about me. I should get my water from Andonis. And I should place my garbage in the bin at the pottery. I am feeling totally overwhelmed. I don't think I can actually live here. Carrying heavy water jugs up the hill worries me. And though Elefteria is very warm and sweet, I know it will be almost impossible to reach her for any problems. I'll try to stay I tell her. But I will need a week to be sure. At this she demurs a little but she seems to understand how strange I feel.

We walk down together to get water from Andonis' house. It is already growing dark and she realizes I have nothing to eat. She takes a plastic bag and fills it with some bread and cheese and olives and tomatoes for me for my first night. On the way back to the house she points out a little goat track that is the quickest route to the beach. It is barely wide enough to walk on.

Andonis is ready to drive Elefteria back to the village where she lives. She seems reluctant to leave me here alone. Come home with me, she invites me. I have a place for you to sleep. And though I'm tempted to come with her, I thank her and refuse. There is a part of me that is aware that it will soon be sunset. I want to sit on the veranda and watch the sun sink into the sea. I want to watch the twilight deepen over the mountain and watch the stars emerge.

She leaves and in a few moments the truck winds away up the mountain road.

My bags are still next to the road where I left them. I carry them up to the house. But I find I am unwilling to unpack. I'm too filled with doubts about whether I can stay. I sit outside looking out over the deepening blue of the bay. I'm certainly here for tonight. I can't even imagine a way to leave. The only telephone in the village is down the winding little footpaths and then walking the length of the beach. I don't know if I could find my way in the dark and even if I could, whom would I call. I asked Elefteria about taxis and she told me they refuse to come down the rough dirt road.

Below the house a dog keeps barking. Voices float across the bay from the village. And suddenly I hear a loud voice calling Andonis' name again and again. I realize it is his paging system. The sounds are coming from a boat anchored at a small dock. The dog goes on barking. I smile wryly at my vision of a serene place. I'm not sure one can be found in this country. The sky fills with stars and a cool breeze caresses my skin. After a long while I go inside and sleep.

I am woken at dawn by the barking of the dog. It is more of a loud squeak than a bark and goes on for about half an hour until any hope of falling asleep again is gone. A wave of hopelessness washes over me. I search the kitchen and find some coffee in the cabinets and prepare it.

As the day continues I slowly begin to unpack my things and explore the little house. The kitchen cabinets are filled with beautiful pottery from Andonis, but bowls and dishes and cups are jammed in among old discolored storage containers and stale crackers and cookies. I throw some things out and rearrange others. I peek under the yellow plastic tablecloth and find a lovely wood and tile table. I use the tablecloth to cover a new pile of things I have placed in the back room. Then I decide it is time to see if I can find my way to the village. I set off on the little footpath. It weaves between prickly plants that brush my ankles and then winds over rocks to an empty house below. The rest of the path crosses the veranda of two small shuttered houses and lands me on a narrow strip of beach. From there I find some rough stairs up and around the rocks. I cross another cove and discover a path that winds up and around more rocks and finally descends to an uninterrupted beach.

I splash along the shore to a little café and order breakfast. I miss the warm greetings from friends that I've grown accustomed to. My own smiles feel forced. Perhaps that's why nobody returns them. I find a little market up a long flight of stairs and make some purchases. There are chairs and umbrellas to rent on the beach. I settle into a beach chair and read a book, feeling strange and isolated. And then I go for a long swim in the clear blue sea hoping it will wash my cares away.

When I reach home I see that my new mattress has come. It stands on its side on the veranda with plastic wrapping to protect it. I suspect Andonis brought it in his truck and wonder if he thinks I can lift the thick double mattress by myself. And though I'm pleased that Elefteria has kept her promise, I am also growing certain that I can't stay here and am hoping it can be returned.

And yet I continue unpacking. The only place for my books is on the kitchen counter and I line them up there. I place my battery operated typewriter on the table. I have brought some candles and place one in each room. There is a non-working refrigerator in the bedroom and I find a cloth to cover it. The Greeks don't seem to throw things away. Perhaps on these small islands there simply isn't any way to dispose of things. Behind the house I find old broken buckets, mattresses and metal bed frames. And yet the house itself is very clean and full of light.

Then I go down to talk to Andonis. Elefteria has told me he will help me with rides to town or any other problems I have. I inquire whether he will be driving to town tomorrow and he says yes. But when I ask what time he will go, he gruffly tells me he doesn't know. And then he goes back to work.

I climb back up to the house and sit outside to watch the sun set into a bank of clouds. I can hear the waves brushing the shore and a goat is bleating somewhere in the hills. Dogs bark and small boats hurry here and there in the harbor. I sit drinking tea and watch my feelings—my fears and doubts and longings. The one thing I am certain of is that I am very tired. I go inside and light the candles. The little house seems to glow. Since all the walls are white, a soft light falls everywhere. A few moments later I blow out all the candles and quickly fall asleep.

Again I wake very early to the barking of the dog. Although it is just after dawn, it is clear it is going to be amazingly hot. I wake to the sea and the mountains and sit on the veranda to meditate. After breakfast I go down to the small beach just below the house and ask Andonis if I can swim there. He laughs and says of course. And then I gather up my courage and talk about my problem with the dog. *Gavyési polí enorís káthi méra.* He barks very early every morning. I carefully looked up the words I didn't know. Andonis explains that the dog barks so early because that is when the boats begin to move about. He doesn't think he can do anything about it, but he'll see. Then I wander along into the village and climb up to the store. The woman who owns the store greets me warmly today. I tell her I am renting Elefteria's house. She speaks some English and we decide we should help each other with Greek and English. And we sit together for awhile outside of the store and chat.

I rent a chair again and swim and read. The old man who rents the chairs also wants to know where I live. He is a cousin of Elefteria, he tells me. He also rents boats and I ask him if there is any way I could rent a boat to use for a few months. Ask Andonis, he tells me. He has four or five boats and will let you use one.

When I reach home, I see that the mattress is no longer on the terrace. When I go inside I see that it has been placed on top of the other mattresses creating a very high bed. Someone has neatly made it up with sheets and blankets. I wonder if Elefteria was here. I run down to ask Andonis. He says it was the son of Elefteria who put the bed inside.

And then I ask about a boat. Yes, he says, you can use the little rowboat. And we smile at each other. I try to tell him about my doubts about living here. And that I'm feeling better. We have been very cautious with one another but I think we are both beginning to feel we could be friends. I ask about his wife who will be coming in a few days. He seems pleased that I've asked and tells me his son, who is fourteen, will also be coming now that the school year is over.

I take a long swim from the beach near the pottery. It is almost like having a private beach below my house. I walk along the shore collecting tiny shells and then climb back up to the house. The blue shutters are open, a gentle breeze is blowing, and for the first time I begin to believe that I have found a home for the coming months.

Late in the night I wake to the clang of goat bells. They sound close by. I climb out of bed and stand in the open doorway. There are about twenty goats grazing just outside the door. They look strong and wild. The pungent smell of thyme fills the air. When they leave I go out and sit on the veranda and gaze at the steep green hills and the deeply cut bay. The sea glimmers with moonlight and all the cicadas sing.

II

I wake to bright sunshine. After a long breakfast of fresh bread and butter and honey and a few cups of steaming coffee, I run down to the pottery and ask Andonis if I can borrow the little boat. He agrees and helps me to carry it to the water. And then he gives me a quick lesson in how to align the ropes that serve as oarlocks. I push off shore into the clear blue sea. For awhile I follow the shoreline and gaze down at the sparkling rocks and tiny fish. And then I row slowly across the bay. I tug the boat up onto the beach.

I swim and sunbathe and swim again. And then I climb up to the little store to buy some groceries—feta cheese cut from a huge block and pasta and olive oil, succulent red tomatoes and peaches. Eggplant and zucchini. Fresh capers and olives from a barrel. With the boat below to load my groceries into, I don't have to worry about how much it all weighs.

Once everything is loaded in the boat, it is time for another swim. And then I slowly row home. I put away my groceries and decide to cook myself a wonderful dinner. I stir-fry zucchini and tomatoes and eggplant. I cook a pot of pasta and grate cheese. And add a lot of lemon juice. As the sun begins to set, I take my dinner out on the veranda where a delicate cool breeze has begun to blow.

People have gathered below on Andonis' terrace. His family has arrived. Villagers keep arriving in small motor boats to welcome them. I know I would be warmly greeted if I went down to join them. But I am too content sitting in the gathering darkness.

It isn't until the next day that I wander down to the pottery. I am introduced to Andonis' wife Maria, a young woman with dark sparkling eyes and curly hair, and to his chubby young son Yianis. I am invited in to have a coffee with the family. Andonis' parents have also come for the summer, a warm elderly couple that I instantly like. We chat in Greek, and I realize how much Greek I will be learning. No one here speaks more than a word or two of English. I sit in the kitchen at a long table. Flies buzz around us and I am offered bread and olives and sweets. The dog Griffi sits at my side and I stroke him and sit listening to an orchestra of Greek, voices rising and falling accompanied by the whisper of the sea just outside the door.

A heat wave has begun and the temperature is about 100 degrees. Today when I come home, I am happy to find the back door that was impossible to open now stands ajar. Not only does the open doorway provide a lovely new view of the hills but it also allows a wonderful breeze to flow through the house. I want to leave it open all the time but realize I will need a screen to keep out insects and snakes. There is a roll of screen in the back room. I quickly look up the word for saw in my dictionary and run down to see if Andonis can lend me one. When he understands what I want it for, he helps me to fit a piece of old wood at the top and bottom of the door frame. Then I cut a large piece of screen and tack it carefully into place.

But now I also have a view of discarded tins and rubbish that is tossed behind the house. Despite the heat, I find a large garbage bag and begin to fill it with shreds of plastic and old rusted pipes, pottery shards and bottles. I drag it down to the trash bin. Then I pull an old metal bedframe out of sight.

I change to a bathing suit and run down to the beach. And then I swim and float on my back gazing up at the bright blue dome of the sky. When I climb back up and turn on the shower, I find that the water that is usually cold is blazing hot, so hot I'd be badly burned if I stood beneath it. So I fill buckets with cool cistern water and return to the shower. I add enough hot water to the buckets to create the perfect temperature. And then I pour the water over my body. Later I go down to talk to Andonis about the water problem. I know the word for hospital in Greek, and he laughs when I tell him I would have to go to the hospital if I showered with that water. He shows me the black plastic pipes that go from the pottery up the cliffs to my house. It is the black pipes that hold the sun's heat, he tells me.

Across the bay and beyond the village is a rocky piece of land. I've been meaning to go exploring there and today I set off. I walk the beach and on the far side I find small footpaths leading out along the rocky point. I walk to the end where the cliffs plunge into the sea. Waves spill over the rocks. Across the bay I can see my house above the sea, with its bright blue shutters open and the mountain rising behind it.

On my way back I find a pile of geranium cuttings, some stems someone has tossed into a pile. Here and there a blossom or bud still clings to the stems. I gather them up and carry them home with me. I've been longing to have some flowers on my veranda but how to get some has eluded me. Now I gently smash the ends of the stems with a stone and remove many of the leaves and blossoms. I plant a few in the stony earth that surrounds the veranda. I walk down to the pottery to ask Andonis if he might have some old chipped pottery that I could use as a planter. He finds me one large pot and even fills it with some good earth for me. I carry it back up the hill stopping every few minutes to rest from its weight. And then I plant the rest of the geraniums. As soon as the sun sets I carry buckets of water from the cistern to water them.

I decide to have dinner in my favorite café on the beach. I sit eating and watching the darkness fold in and the sky begin to fill with stars. The sea barely murmurs against the shore. Finally I thank the restaurant owner and we call out *kaliníxta, kaliníxta,* goodnight, to one another and I walk down the beach toward my house. I take off my shoes and splash in the warm shallows. A family has moved into the little house whose veranda I must cross. I've spoken to them and they have assured me I am welcome at any time. But as I approach the house, a dark shape looms in the darkness blocking my path. It takes only a second to realize it is Griffi. I've never seen him away from the pottery before. He must have seen my dark house and come out to wait for me. He wriggles with excitement and jumps up on my chest. And I pat him happily. Together we find the tiny footpaths up the cliff. At the lane to my house, Griffi stops. I give him a pat goodbye.

I find my water situation has changed again. Now a pump has been hooked up. And the water is quite cold. Elefteria has told me the hot water heater will come very soon now. So I heat a few large pots of water on the stove and shower by pouring them over my head.

I go out on the veranda to look at the geraniums. They look very healthy and are already beginning to make some tiny new leaves. I water the dry soil and can almost hear them eagerly drink.

Andonis would like to learn some English. Often tourists find their way to the pottery and it would be helpful for him to be able to speak to them. So every now and then I try to teach him a few words of English. Each word feels strange and foreign in his mouth. He is shy of trying to say a new word. And he finds it almost impossible to repeat the sounds I make. I show him how to shape his mouth and where to place his tongue. But it doesn't seem to help. And then suddenly he reveals that he can read English. I'm amazed and hurry to find us paper and pen. When I write down the same words he has been struggling over, he can pronounce them easily.

I often take the bus up to the central villages and spend the day sitting in cafés reading and writing and sipping cool drinks and then walking the beautiful footpaths. Today as I sit in a little café in Pano Petali, someone is practicing the piano in a nearby house. The notes are single notes played very slowly, perhaps by a child. They ring out clearly into the still air.

Then I walk and take photos of the old walls and the fig trees and the sea far below. I also carry a sketchbook. I would like to paint every stone in these beautiful old walls, to paint the dry grasses and lose myself in the tans and yellows and beiges. I want to paint the green leaves of this eucalyptus, its bark striped with gray and tan and blue and pink. To cling to beauty is another form of suffering, the Buddhist monks say. A flock of crows flies over the dome of the church and across the startlingly blue sky. A yellow butterfly floats by. The etched curving lines in the pavement where I am walking are filled with flower pollen the color of coral. The shadow of the eucalyptus leaves plays over the footpath, more graceful than the leaves themselves.

I follow a footpath to a lovely little *eklisía,* a chapel set in a small valley. Inside it is cool and serene. I leave a few drachma on the table and choose a slim yellow candle to light. Each tiny chapel on this island remains unlocked. There are said to be three hundred and sixty-five of them. And then I sit in the little courtyard that encircles the chapel. As though in a dream, I see a group of huge steer walking unattended down the road. I have only encountered these massive animals once before and ran headlong down a path to a nearby chapel. This time I feel safely out of reach of their long curving horns.

It isn't until evening that I return to Vathi. I find that the little monastery along the shore is having a *panayíri,* a small festival. Its doorway and windows are framed in laurel branches and a large crowd has gathered. Inside the priest is conducting a service and the chanting and prayers fill the air. The traditional huge round loaves of bread are sliced and passed around, held aloft until everyone has received a large chunk. Then a line forms for the meal. I join some friends who have come for the *panayíri* and we wait together. Finally we are ushered into a room with long tables. We are served chickpea soup and bread and wine and cheese and olives. The atmosphere is festive and the men and women serving the meal come around frequently to refill the wine glasses. Toasts are made again and again. And every few moments everyone stops eating and drinking to clang their spoons noisily against their glasses to express thanks and appreciation.

After everyone has eaten, violin and guitar music begins. There is singing and dancing. I see the woman from the little grocery store, Katarina. Her husband Panayotis is also there. He is a sea captain with a small *karavaíki,* a little boat that circles the island any day that the sea is calm. Wearing a warm smile and his sailing cap, he dances proudly with his beautiful teenage daughters while the music plays and the chapel bells ring out.

I walk home late at night along the beach with a flashlight. As I approach the little house whose veranda I must cross, the outside light suddenly goes on. A man who lives there has spotted me and wants to make my walk easier. We call out greetings to one another. As I search the dark hillside for the little footpath that leads up, I suddenly find Griffi by my side. He yelps with excitement and I stroke his head again and again. We climb up together to the little lane to my house and then reluctantly part.

I have grown to feel so completely at home here. In the morning I stop at the little beach café and the young woman who runs it invites me to have a fresh orange juice. Then I walk to the bus stop and sit on the wall beside a Greek woman. We chat for awhile and she compliments me on my Greek. Then she takes a large *mizéthra* cheese from her bag and presents it to me. This is the wonderful creamy cheese of this island that is often placed on top of a Greek salad. I thank her again and again.

When I get off the bus in the central village I realize I need to refrigerate my cheese. I go to a café and ask the owner if I could leave it in his refrigerator. He agrees and I go off to do some errands. In the bookstore I spot a huge bundle of bubble wrapping in a back room. I ask Maria, the bookstore owner, if I might possibly buy it. Instead she gathers it up and tells me she is happy to give it to me.

I walk up a beautiful lane to my favorite breakfast café and order fruit and thick wonderful yogurt and honey. And cappuccino. Bougainvillea spills over the walls. A few donkeys pass by. And the bright sun beams down.

Finally I take the bus back to Vathi and wend my way back to the pottery. I have bought a wonderful circular bottle with a deep blue glaze from Andonis. I want to send it to my son in America. Andonis has warned me that the pottery will break and I shouldn't try to mail it. But I've decided to try anyway. I show him the bubble paper and we wrap the bottle in many protective layers. Then we place it in a box and carefully seal it with tape. *Kalo taxídi,* a good journey to you, we both say to the box. We smile at each other and he wishes me luck.

After a long wonderful swim I go up to my house. I gather up my paints and sketchbook and sit on the veranda. And then I paint a picture of the little bay beneath my house. I paint the mountains on either side almost meeting and the deep blue of the sea.

Andonis' wife Maria now goes in a small motorboat each morning from the pottery to the little village across the bay. Her son Yannis takes her. She has a little shop there where she sells pottery. This morning I see them beginning to load the boat with crates of pottery, pitchers and bowls and cups glazed with blue and brown and green.

I run down to ask if I can also come. Welcome, she tells me. I help them finish loading. We also take all the large empty jugs. Our drinking water comes from a deep well in the village. Yannis is proud to be the captain of the little boat and we roar across the bay.

Today I discover that the little *karavaíki* is leaving from Vathi in a few minutes. It is going to a place named Fikiada for a few hours. I greet Panayotis and happily jump aboard. We land below a lovely chapel. There is a long beach where everyone heads for a swim. I visit the chapel and then join the others in the sparkling blue sea.

The island begins to fill with tourists. Ferryboats arrive each day with crowds of people. All the rooms on the island are now filled. I can feel the pulse beat speed up. The buses race down the curving island roads, their radios pouring out music from the open windows. Inside, the crowds of people brace themselves around the deep curves. In the central village all the roads are very narrow and lines of cars have to rapidly back up and try to find a place to pull over to let the buses go by.

More and more people arrive at the pottery until it begins to seem like a little village. Maria's mother is now here, and also the brother of Andonis and his wife and children. In the evenings their friends arrive to visit and sip wine and ouzo. As I sit on my veranda, a chorus of Greek voices floats up. I listen and watch the moon slowly cross the sky. Then one by one the boats leave and the lights flicker out. Cicadas sing and in the hills the goat bells ring. At last I go inside to sleep, serenaded by the gentle murmur of the sea.

Today is warm and cloudy. I stay all day in Vathi, puttering around the house. I collect goat droppings to fertilize my geraniums. They are all beginning to bud. Then I walk down to the beach and find a friend there. She tells me I look glamorous. Yesterday I went to a beautician to get my hair styled. A few days ago in a fit of desperation,

I had cut it myself. The beautician evened out the jagged cuts I had made and I was pleased with the results.

I spend the afternoon sitting on a sea wall and painting a picture of the little monastery. I work with watercolors. Almost any mistake I make can be painted over. I love adding layer after layer of color. And then I add a touch of each color everywhere—bright red or yellow in the sea and the hills and the rock walls. Or touches of blue and green in the trees and in the mountains. Flecks of white everywhere. I often think how fulfilling it must be to truly have artistic talent. What I can do is so limited and even then I feel it is only luck if something turns out right.

The next morning I wake to wild wind and clouds and a sea filled with whitecaps. For the first time I close the windows against the wind. I notice that everyone seems to be gone from the pottery. It is rare for them to be away so I go down with a few large plastic bags. I've spoken to Andonis about all the rubbish on the beach— plastic and cigarette butts, stray beer cans and bottles. He responded by telling me the beach is clean. So now that I have the place to myself, I wander along picking up debris and then dragging it to the garbage bin. A far corner of the beach has been used as a dump site. I go up and get more plastic bags and clear away that rubbish as well.

I swim for awhile and then walk the shoreline collecting tiny perfect shells. And then I climb up to my house to shower and dress. There is a *panayíri* today in a tiny remote village called Heronisos. The little boat was supposed to depart from Vathi, but when I reach the dock I find that because of the strong winds, it will leave from the main port. A bus is just about to leave so I jump on amidst the crowds. When I reach the port I find the boat just ready to depart.

The boat rocks in the waves, the radio sings out and we hug the coastline until we reach the little village. Many people have already gathered there at the small monastery. I see the postmaster and he greets me by name for the first time and hands me a small glass of ouzo. I watch the long ceremony, the children carrying candles, the women kissing the icon. And the cutting of the huge round loaves of bread. The postmaster makes certain I get seated for the meal and keeps filling my wine glass. Even though I know almost no one, I feel very at home.

Later I sit on the beach in the cool night air. A half moon rises over the mountains. And the sea rushes into shore. And then the *karavaíki* is ready to return. The captain's daughter has brought pitchers of wine aboard and serves us all. Loud screechy music blares from a radio and the stars gleam and the little boat tosses wildly in the waves. And then Panayotis and his daughter give me a ride home in their truck. They are used to the rough road to the pottery and deliver me to my door at about 3:00 a.m.

I sit outside for awhile in the moonlight and starlight. Everyone is sleeping below. I can hear the bells of the grazing goats somewhere nearby. The little house is filled with the soft light of candles. And finally I go inside and blow them out and climb into bed.

In the morning two men arrive bringing my hot water heater. I've regretted asking for one for heating the water on the stove has worked fine. But I celebrate by taking a long shower, the warm water pouring effortlessly over me.

Because it is the height of the tourist season, there are day trips now to other islands on small hydrofoils. I decide to visit Serifos, a nearby island that I haven't visited in a number of years. The port seems crowded and much more developed than the last time I was here. But I hop on a bus for the Chora, a tiny upper village with a tumble of white stairways and tiny lanes and gleaming white houses. Flowers and snowy-white doves are everywhere. I climb up and up to the three little churches at the top of the mountain. To reach the highest one there are white stairs interrupted a few times by bare rock. The rocks are whitewashed like the stairs to show the way. At the top are mountain ridges and soaring views down over the port. And far out to sea a wild wind blows. Cicadas sing. I am the only one here.

I return by the little footpaths that wind through the village. There is a serpentine road that winds back to the port that interrupts the footpath again and again. But at each point where it is necessary to cross the road, the footpath is marked with whirls of white paint. And when I finally reach the port there is that wonderful feeling of being able to look back at where one has been. From the beach I can see the little churches on the peak of the mountain. They seem impossibly far away.

I have dinner at the port and wait for the hydrofoil to bring me back home. Then I take two buses over the curving dark roads. When I finally climb up to my house I'm ready for a long sleep.

In the morning when I go out to water the geraniums, I find two small crimson blossoms. It seems amazing that only a few weeks ago they didn't even have roots. I ride to the village in the boat with Maria and Yannis. And then I visit in the little pottery shop with Maria. I have received a letter from my son saying that the wine bottle arrived intact. She has been asking about it every few days and is delighted to hear it arrived unbroken. She tells me how restless she gets in the tiny shop and is happy that she will only be here for a few more weeks. Then school will begin and she and Yannis will return to the central village where they have a large house. I ask her if she would like to have more children and her eyes dance at the thought. She smiles and tells me how much she loves babies. Now and then she gently corrects my awkward Greek. And I teach her a few phrases in English.

I take a bus to the main village to do a few errands. And then I catch a bus back. Instead of riding all the way to the village, I ask the driver to stop at the top of the rough dirt road that winds down to my house. And then I begin slowly walking home. As I round a deep curve in the road, I see a mother goat and two kids. One of the young goats panics at the sight of me and runs far down the road ahead of me. When it finally stops and realizes it is alone, it bleats poignantly. A very large male goat with long curving horns also appears in the road. We gaze at each other and I stand still to show him I mean no harm. He is rugged and wild looking. Finally he leaps away into the bushes and disappears from sight.

After a shower, I go down to the beach café for dinner. The setting sun sinks into a cloud. Then it reappears for a moment glowing crimson and once again is lost in the clouds. The ducks have climbed high up on the beach to sleep and the waves wash in softly. I sip wine and eat chickpea balls and a wonderful Greek salad and then chat with the café owner. And finally we say goodnight and I walk slowly home along the beach. I have left an outside light on at my house and can see it brightly shining from the darkness of the hill. But as I walk on, it vanishes. Perhaps it is the curve of the beach or the hills that hide it from view again and again. It seems like a premonition for soon I will be leaving. Early in the fall all the villagers depart either to return to Athens or to move back to one of the inner villages. The cafés and little shops close and all the rooms are shuttered and deserted. As if in answer to my thoughts, the light of my little house flickers brightly for a moment and then it disappears. I am left with only the stars and the sand and the sea.

PART III

Forgiveness

Southeast Asia Sketchbook

My father had many sketchbooks. Some were large and some were small enough to fit into his pocket. I loved to browse through them. I'd find a tree, a sloping shoulder, a woman's sorrowful face. I felt he was enabling me to see through his eyes. These words are sketches of a journey in Southeast Asia. I dedicate them to my father.

BALI

A gecko pokes out its head from behind my bathroom mirror. Bulging eyes. It emerges slowly. Then it catches each moth and insect from the wall. I watch wings disappear into a wide mouth.

⁓

The barman is speaking about the magic of Lombok. They can put a glass bottle in your stomach, he tells me, or turn your mouth into a weird grimace, steal from you without your knowing or fill you with sensual desire.

He says there is white magic also, magic that can make you fly. Like magic mushrooms, I ask, and he laughs. With mushrooms you only feel like you fly, he says. And no one can see you.

He talks of herbal medicines that can make a woman young again and beautiful, that make a woman's vagina like that of a virgin.

And he speaks of frogs. Only the males sing. If one sings off key, the others complain and nip at him.

⁓

Two large carved ducks beside the road and a shop with a sign reading Various of Duck.

⁓

I like watching the women cook in the *warungs,* small booths set up along the beaches and the roads. They mash peanuts, chili and garlic. Then they add water to make peanut sauce. They chop tofu. They slice rolled banana leaves which contain a portion of cooked rice. The food is arranged like an offering.

⁓

Always somewhere a gamelon is playing, relentless and full of sorrow and of joy, a clear stream of melody moving through the slow afternoons.

⌒

The cows here are slender and graceful as deer. They graze beneath the coconut trees. And beyond them is the sea.

⌒

There is a small soft brown lump on my bed. I learn it is a dropping from a gecko. When a gecko calls seven times in its cracked voice, it is said to bring luck.

⌒

Warm rain today. A woman is washing her feet in a mud puddle. A child walks beside the road holding a large banana leaf over her head to keep off the rain. A flock of tan ducks is shepherded down the road.

⌒

I move to a bungalow on a quiet back road of Ubud. The old man of the family welcomes me with a huge pot of steaming tea. He returns a few moments later to wipe our faint footprints from the shining tiles of my porch.

⌒

The villagers are gathered in the road in the twilight to laugh and chat. The men hold their prize rooster, stroking it proudly. Other roosters, each in a curved bamboo cage, are set by the roadside. I am told this is to keep them from becoming bored.

A boy named Nyoman has brought me here on his motorbike to see the heron. They come at dusk, hundreds of them, to this small village where they sleep in the trees. They settle on the branches like large white blossoms.

We ride slowly homeward through the dusky night past rice terraces. Beside the road young women are bathing in the stream. Fireflies flicker in the darkening sky.

⌒

Each day I stop for awhile to watch a huge bull that is being built. It has been carved from wood. Then it is covered with wicker and soft coconut husks. Then a layer of burlap and finally soft black velour. A man glues pieces of red felt around its large eyes and mouth. Its legs are decorated in gold. Its large red penis is erect. The bull will be used for a cremation. The body will be placed inside and then it will be set aflame.

⌒

A woman stoops beside a large pile of dirt. She has a basket on her head. She scoops dirt and empties it over her head into the basket until it is overflowing. Now with each scoop, the dirt falls all around her. Finally she rises with the grace of a dancer and disappears down a small lane.

I go to stay by the sea. There is a full moon now and the nights are filled with a gentle mysterious mist. The sea and the sky seem wedded and the air is balmy.

At night the geckos call loudly. And there is a night bird that calls persistently. Music from the distant cafés. Heat. Later a few mosquitoes circle my room. And finally the predawn Muslim chanting. Roosters celebrating the first light. I don't know how to sleep on this island.

I walk down the road in the warm rain. The mountains are lost in mist. The green fields of rice gleam and the thatched roofs look washed clean. I walk past the strange swayback Balinese pigs, their tails flicking as they root in the grasses. Two small girls with wicker brooms sweep bright orange petals from the path.

I buy a carved wooden Buddha. And a small gamelon. I go to a shipping office where two women work for almost an hour preparing a package for me to mail home. They cut down a box until it is the right size and use shredded paper for packing. Then they seal the box and cover it with heavy plastic. With a sharpened stick they punch holes all around the edges of the box and weave blue plastic ribbon to secure it firmly.

Two mahogany butterflies are dancing in the morning light.

In Bali the first child is named Wayan. This is true for a girl or for a boy. The second born is named Made. The third is Nyoman and the fourth is Ketut. If a fifth child is born the name Wayan is given once again. Then Made. And Nyoman and Ketut.

A stream runs just beyond the door of my bungalow. At dawn the women come to wash their clothes there. I wake each day to laughter and chattering voices.

I visit an old Balinese village, a village of the *Bali Aga*. This is a place where the old ways are still intact. A *Bali Aga* who marries someone from outside the village must move away.

⁓

The nights are a cacophony of geckos calling their own names and frogs and crickets and rain.

⁓

I scrape my toe open on a rock on the main road of Ubud. There are few sidewalks and walking consists of trying to dodge traffic by walking on a rough stony shoulder. After each rain it is muddy and slippery. Several times a day I wash the cut and apply antiseptic, hoping that soon a scab will form. But nothing dries in this humidity. Nothing heals.

⁓

I stop and chat with a woman who is sitting beside the road making tiny woven baskets. First she makes careful cuts in a banana leaf. Then it is intricately folded and fastened with a sharpened bamboo needle. I sit beside her and she shows me how to fold and sew.

⁓

Black rice pudding is served bubbling hot. It is sprinkled with sugar and coconut milk.

～

Water buffalo roam the paths of this village. I follow the sounds of gamelons and find a large orchestra rehearsing with their teacher. Someone beckons me in and I listen for hours to metal clappers and gamelons and loud drumming that rises and falls in waves. I wonder if I am being changed by this music, the strange rhythms, the relentlessness.

～

Offerings are placed at every temple, every crossroad, every doorway. An arrangement of flowers and woven leaves and rice grains. They are sprinkled with holy water.

～

Clinging to the wide mouth of a cave is a vast colony of bats. Their bodies touch and overlap and cling. Some are sleeping, some moving about and others are cleaning their young. A priest is chanting and people sit on the earth and pray.

～

My stomach is ailing and I am given snake fruit or *salak* to eat. First it must be boiled for fifteen minutes. The taste is bland and pleasant. By the next day I am well.

⌒

The *Kechak* dance has a human orchestra. Dozens of barechested men sit in a circle, their voices chanting and croaking and beating. These are sounds I hadn't known a human voice could make.

⌒

In the mountains the air is cool and moist. Bright splashes of blue morning glories amidst a jungle of greenery. Monkeys with small tufts on their heads are sitting in the road.

⌒

I stand in the crowd and watch giant statues of gods carried aloft on frames. It takes many men to support them. Orchestras pass with gamelons and drums and resounding gongs. The women are dressed in sarongs and temple scarves. They carry tall intricate arrangements of fruit on their heads.

⌒

The village boys are filled with longing. Ketut wants a bag to carry his books. Wayan wants a watch he can wear into the sea. They want my scuffed sandals and my sweater and my daughter's photograph. We have nothing, they tell me. I gesture toward the fringe of shining white sand and the sea. We have nothing, they say again.

At dawn I run down to the beach where a boat is waiting. It is long and narrow, carved from a mango tree. We motor far out to sea until we find the dolphins. The sun is rising and dolphins are leaping all around us.

Stacks of firewood are piled between the legs of the huge black bull and set aflame. The crowd laughs and cheers. The bull's bright necklaces and golden halter are the first to turn to ash.

When it grows dark I carry in the mosquito coil that has been lit for me and left on my porch. Then I get a cup of hot lemon juice and honey and sit by the sea. A full moon is sailing through the clouds.

PENANG

It is a long train ride from Singapore to Penang. I sit between cars by the open door in the warm wind. I am wondering if I should leave my luggage behind and jump off the train to follow one of the paths that wind away through the trees.

~

It is night and a group of boys are balancing a huge and multi-colored flag on a long pole. They place the end of the pole on their foreheads and their shoulders. They pass it from one to another. There is a full moon and a flag floating against the sky.

BANGKOK

A butterfly with a delicate watercolor painting on its wings. Fine pen lines and then a wash of pale rose and yellow.

~

At Wat Po I pay thirty baht and set two small bright birds free. A woman has a cage filled with birds. "This will bring you good fortune," she tells me.

~

The *klongs* are bordered by flimsy wooden houses with decks suspended above the river. Pots filled with bright flowers and laundry hung out to dry. Dogs and cats and birds in cages. Children playing in the muddy green water. My long-tailed boat passes beside a small café where a young girl washes lettuce in the river. Bougainvillea spilling across a wall. A few modern apartment buildings. Gilded shining monasteries. And everywhere there are people cooking, doing their laundry, sewing, eating, sleeping beside these milky waters.

—◦

When I want to go somewhere in this vast city, I ask the person at the desk of the guesthouse to write it down for me. So few people speak English. Even when I learn to say the word in Thai, I am seldom understood. I stand like a child, clutching a note in my hand.

—◦

The *tuk-tuk* drivers are often new in town. They don't know their way much better than I do. This one gets more and more disgruntled when he can't find the address of the place I want to go. He is sweating profusely and wiping his face again and again with an old kerchief. Suddenly I remember I have a travel tissue in my bag. He watches in the rear view mirror as I carefully unfold it and then hand it to him. He wipes his face, looking amazed by the cool moist cloth. Then he grins back at me.

—◦

King works at the guesthouse. She spent her childhood living on the *klongs*. "I longed to be in America," she tells me. "I knew that there I could leave my house and go for a walk." From her house the only way to leave was by boat. And only one boat came by each day.

WAT PA NANACHAT

As a lay woman at this monastery, I am provided with clothes to wear. A white sleeveless underblouse and a white short-sleeved blouse. For a skirt there is a very wide circular black cloth that I step into and then tie at my waist like a sarong.

I have two of everything. Each day I wash the clothes from the day before and hang them out in the sun to dry.

I open the bathroom door gently. On the inside is a hook where a clear shower cap hangs. Inside the cap are two immense spiders.

Squirrels and chipmunks playing on the forest floor. A velvety blackbird with a white circle on its back is singing on a branch.

I rise for meditation just before it grows light. I sweep the forest pathways with a broom of stiff straw.

⸺◦

In the predawn light the villagers come with large baskets of food to offer to the monks. The women cook in the open air kitchen. There is one meal a day at 9:30 a.m. The food is nutritious and plentiful. There is rice and tofu and vegetables. Salads and sweets and fresh tropical fruits. After the meal when all the dishes have been washed, the women and children lie down on bamboo mats to talk and visit and sleep.

⸺◦

The meditation huts are built on stilts. Around each stilt is a small cement moat to keep insects away. Today at tea the monks are talking about the ways that ants can cross water. Some find a raft, perhaps a bit of straw to ride on. The smallest ones can walk across the surface. Some wait for the wind and leap.

⸺◦

There is a meditation path beside my hut. At dusk I place a candle at each end and walk slowly back and forth. The candles glow and somewhere in the trees an owl gives a low hoot. The earth is warm beneath my feet.

⌒

There is a small lizard on the tree trunk. It has a brown and white striped back and an orange tail. It curls its tail and then flicks it back and forth like a cat . . . that same feeling of energy gathering.

⌒

It is evening now and there is a sudden unexpected rain. It rustles in the trees. Today I watered the plants around the ajahn's *kuti* for they were withering in the sun. And now the rain becomes a downpour clattering on the metal roof. A bolt of lightning and then thunder.

MEKONG RIVER

In Thailand I hear the word *farang* again and again. It means foreigner. Ke owns the little guesthouse on the river where I am staying. She and I become friends. "The *farang* will go to the monastery tonight," she tells someone. "The *farang* took a shower," her son calls to her as I emerge from the outdoor shower stall.

⌒

My bungalow has a mattress on a platform and a warm quilt and pillow. A gauzy mosquito net. The windows are open spaces.

There are a few nails to hang things on. From its small porch I can see the river and the hills of Laos beyond it.

⁓

This morning there is shooting in Laos. Ke grabs her son and runs inside.

⁓

I take a bus that follows the river. Now and then there are trees carved into shapes. I see a water buffalo, a large peacock in the branches, a long-tailed boat carrying many people, a deer, an elephant, a dolphin, a giraffe. The Thais watch my delight and make certain I don't miss anything.

⁓

Tonight there is fire in the mountains of Laos. The peaks are outlined with a bright orange glow. Now and then a flame leaps up into the dark sky.

⁓

At night the village dogs are released and guard the dusty quiet roads. I walk filled with dread as they snap and growl at my legs.

⟞⟝

There is a small monastery down the road from the guesthouse. Only two or three monks are living there on a dusty piece of earth above the river. The buildings are simple wooden structures in need of paint. There is a feeling of peace.

⟞⟝

List of gifts I buy at the Laotian refugee shop and mail to America:
- 1 shirt
- 1 doll
- 2 embroidered pillow covers that depict the Laotian villagers driven from home by soldiers and crossing the river to Thailand
- 2 carved turtles

⟞⟝

Twilight. The boys of the village and a few men come down to the river to bathe. One boy first hangs his towel carefully on a branch. He makes a few fierce punches into the air and then stands on his hands. Now he is ready to bathe.

⟞⟝

This is the day of Buddha's enlightenment. In the evening the villagers gather at the small monastery. There are many children and everyone carries flowers and candles and incense. A monk gives a talk in Thai. The only word I can understand is *farang*. He says it several times and everyone turns to look at me. This time the word is a welcome.

After the talk everyone pours out into the moonlit night and we slowly circle the temple three times. Then we place our candles on the stone walls. The flowers and incense are also placed there. The ceremony has ended and everyone disappears into the darkened streets. I linger on, watching the candles flicker in the darkness. A monk is standing in the temple doorway and I place my hands to my forehead and bow my head. He bows his head in return.

⁓

I sit on the banks and watch the river flowing by. The Mekong moves swiftly and impartially. It sweeps everything along in its current. I watch my thoughts arise and disappear.

Sleeping Like the Buddha

Reflections on a Meditation Retreat

DAY 1

Peace permeates this northern California monastery. The peacocks are still here giving their strange plaintive cries. As I walk through the fields I see pheasants and rabbits. I walk past a covey of quail and they do not startle away.

I sit in the meadow in the cool evening air waiting for the first evening sitting. I've been waiting so long for this retreat, hoping it is a chance to go forth into some deeper understanding.

DAY 2

Last night I fell out of bed. It felt more as if the bed dropped me. The mattress is completely unsupported on the sides. In the middle of the night I woke up chilly and reached down for a blanket on the floor. I promptly landed on top of it.

A smoke alarm with a weak battery emits a high-pitched beep at intervals of a few moments. I sleep and wake to its call. I find myself seeking glimpses of the watcher as I drift again and again into sleep. Sleep is a dark peaceful cloak that folds me inside it. The watcher remains awake.

Last night the monk spoke about the word templum, a consecrated space marked out on the ground within which one observes the movements of nature. Whatever enters a templum is taken note of . . . stars, moon, shadow, bird, insect. Its root is the same as temple and contemplation.

A warm gentle wind blows. This retreat feels different. It feels simpler. I feel less resistance to conforming, less desire to be anyone special. There is nothing much that I expect.

When Ajahn Chah, the old Thai master, was asked how he was, his answer was that he was good enough.

Walking toward the meditation hall, I have a pang of missing the two nuns who were present at last year's retreat. Their radiance changed the universe for me. I hadn't known such beauty was possible.

White dried grasses
and a tree
that sings
whenever I pass

DAY 3

Peacocks mourning in the rain.

Last night the monk spoke of emotional proliferation, conceptual proliferation . . . all those thoughts, desires, aversions that we bring to everything. He tells us the story of the ex-monk who walked three miles in the middle of the night to telephone his friend. You've got to help me, he says. I am going to murder that peacock.

This morning he speaks of Buddha's temptation and the many forms that *Mara*, the one who tempts, can take. The third temptation is responsibility, taking the form of Buddha's elderly father. He is crying and pleading for his son to come home.

A chaos of dreams last night and somehow all the choices I make are wrong ones. I wake wondering what about *metta*, what about loving kindness toward myself.

There is a woman here whose wheelchair sounds like a Tibetan bell. And a blind woman who moves like a dancer. All that arises ceases and is not self, the monk says. I wonder what that makes them think and feel.

DAY 4

The smoke alarm batteries have been replaced and the nights grow peaceful. Some of the people present had come for only three days and now the group is smaller.

The nun spoke last night and said she had a happy moment when she realized she would never be happy, that it wasn't possible. Isn't this the realization of the first noble truth.

Our retreat is housed at a large Chinese monastery. This morning I work in the kitchen. There are two other women from the retreat and the Chinese women. There are caldrons of food to cut and wash. The cook uses a gigantic wok. It takes muscle to stir the food with a spatula as large as a shovel. The washing of vegetables is meticulous. The cutting must be done at certain angles and someone gives us a brief demonstration each time we are to cut a new vegetable. There are seemingly endless pots and bowls for us to wash. We end up wet and tired and smiling.

The nun says that by the fourth day on a retreat, we are so worn down by lack of sleep and submitting to a strange environment that we begin to surrender. We have been rising at five in the morning. The day and evening are divided into forty-five minute periods of sitting meditation followed by a walking meditation. The monk or the nun gives a morning or evening talk. Otherwise silence is maintained during the retreat.

DAY 5

Last night the monk spoke of the stillness that comes from concentration. And yet that is not enough. We can use that stillness to investigate. He describes putting the word *mother* at the center of the stillness when he was a young monk and watching the chaos that ensued. He suggests looking at our angers, our fears, our desires, our aversions . . . learning to know them, to recognize them and to be able to let them go.

I've been hard on myself the last day or so. Self-critical. I don't know why. Maybe looking at it, I will be able to let it go. I even have a toothache I got from clenching my teeth in my sleep. I remember a strange jarring night. I felt as if electric jolts were running through me.

The monk says in making decisions, listen to the heart. The mind can go on and on arguing with itself but the heart doesn't listen anyway. It knows what it wants.

DAY 6

The nun speaks of the formation of an intention. It can be for an hour or a day or much longer. The formation of an intention of loving kindness is the example she gives. As she speaks, I begin to realize the vastness of what she is speaking about. I've always believed our sensitivity is formed by our past and once it is formed it remains unchanged. But monastic life entails a constant attention and awareness. Sensitivity is continuously being refined. I speak excitedly to the monk about my realization and the hope it seems to offer for humanity. Yes, he agrees. It can create miracles.

All at once the retreat seems to be moving too quickly. Today is my last day of working in the kitchen. We spend hours pinching the ends off oriental peas. I like dealing with these huge quantities of food amidst the Chinese women. We sit on low stools like peasants. Today is warmer and for awhile we take our bowls of peas outside and work in the sunlight.

This morning the nun led a meditation on loving kindness. She used as a gauge of lovingness her feelings for squirrels and rabbits.

She tries to apply that tenderness to herself and to all others. All day I have been imagining myself as a rabbit, that innocent and vulnerable.

I want to think much more about the formation of intentions. I want to make it a part of my life. And I want to write of the monk's talk last night. For awhile he spoke about the practice of investigating the watcher. Who is watching, he asked us. Who is it that is watching. I was first instructed in this practice many years ago by a Korean monk. And though my progress has been slow and halting, I've never forgotten the question. I've spoken to the monk about it from time to time and he has gently encouraged me to go on asking.

As he talked I jotted down phrases, fearful of losing them. Each word seemed precious. He spoke of the tremendous sacrifice of this path which entails letting go of everything. He spoke of abiding in the place that is no place. This is a path, he told us, that requires constant relinquishment, relinquishment that will take you the whole way. Sometimes he seemed to be looking at me. And once he said, I don't know if I should be telling you this. After he left the meditation hall, I put my head to the floor and silent sobs ran through me.

This afternoon I finally walk through the sheep meadow to the stream. This is a place of great beauty. The stream has many voices. Now and then I look up startled, thinking someone is speaking just around the bend. I imagine having a hut here where I could sit each day and listen to the stream.

Tonight the monk tells us about a great Chinese Buddhist master. He was twice beaten and left for dead when he was a very old man, beaten by the Red Chinese who wanted to put an end to Buddhism in China. His disciples were bewildered by how their master seemed to cling to life. Finally they said to him, Master you are very old and almost all your bones are broken. Why do you hang on so to your body and your life. Why not let it go now. He explained to them that the karma of his killers would be too great were he to die from their blows. And so he lived on and was not beaten again.

The monk speaks of neither believing your thoughts nor disbelieving. Instead he tells us to hold them up for examination.

Celibacy in India is called *Brahacariya*. It means to walk with God.

DAY 7

The last few days the peacocks have been displaying their glorious tails. Then they turn their backs. Beneath the circle of feathers is a miracle of down and color that I've never seen before.

Lately I find myself thinking of a pilgrimage to the sacred places of India.

Early evening and drizzling. I take a long walk on a path across these green meadows. I had expected the weather to be hot and looked forward to it. But this mist seems gentle and somehow appropriate.

I walk slowly toward the meditation hall and the evening talk, wondering if I am worthy of receiving so much.

DAY 8

Last night the nun spoke about what it was like to become a nun and the limitations that life requires. She had been a dancer who enjoyed her work and her friends. But slowly she grew bored and discontent with continually pleasing herself. She knew life had a deeper meaning and came to the monastery to find it.

She spoke of her wild inner battles and the chaos of resistance she struggled with. Again and again she told herself, Trust this chaos, trust this wild energy for it will set you free.

I had known that many of the monks and nuns had been dreamers and wanderers and rebels. And I wondered how they were able to deal with their rebelliousness. She provided me with a careful description of what her experience had been. It seemed to me she was describing rebellion against rebelliousness and the deep resulting joy. The rebelliousness doesn't die. It changes its object. It begins to serve a deeper morality. I've often longed for a greater self-discipline. I feel she has provided me with a map.

Sometimes my life seems such a long journey. When I was in my twenties someone taught me to trust my feelings. It was an important lesson, one that guided me for years. And now there is the unlearning. There is Buddhism which teaches the impermanence of feelings. Everything that arises ceases and is not self.

There is an eighty-three year old woman attending this retreat. Last night she requested a birthday blessing.

A bluebird is sitting on a branch.

The monk tells us there will be an all night sitting tonight. He will be offering blessings to those who are ill, those who have recently died. I hand in a slip of paper with my parents' names written on it. For awhile there is sadness. Whose sadness is this. I watch it arise and cease.

DAY 9

Last night we meditated until 3:00 a.m. and then recited the morning chants. The monk had made it clear we didn't need to stay all night if we were tired but I think all of us stayed. The night was fluid and timeless. Tea was served at midnight and then we talked with the monk for awhile. And then we continued sitting.

I hadn't expected to attend the whole sitting. But I found I couldn't leave. The sense of community was moving. The meditation was still and deep. At times I rose to go outside to do a walking meditation. The rain had stopped and the night was very cold. I wore a shirt and two sweaters topped with a sweatshirt, all the warm clothes I had brought. I walked slowly back and forth in the darkness and the silence. A full moon sailed in and out of the clouds.

Today the schedule is relaxed to allow us time to rest. And our tiredness and the pouring rain make the day feel slow and peaceful.

I nap for an hour in the afternoon. And just before falling asleep, I realize the answer to the question the Korean monk gave me so long ago. The realization is a quiet one. It changes nothing. And yet everything has changed.

DAY 10

Shoes are lined up in pairs outside the door of the meditation hall. One pair is as small as a child's. It belongs to a young Japanese woman. I have watched her creating lovely intricate flower arrangements. She places them on the altar and in each room where we gather.

The monk talks about a period in which he felt as if he were in a gray box. He was puzzled at his own discontent until he realized it was the *I* that imprisoned him. *Who is meditating* and *who am I* were the questions that allowed the spaciousness to return.

Buddha says the greatest happiness is letting go of the concept of *I am*.

Conceit in Buddhism is believing *I am* whether you believe yourself to be wonderful or terrible or mediocre.

DAY 11

As I meditate there is an image that keeps recurring. It is a moment at the end of my marriage when I ran sobbing down a path into a thicket. My husband followed me and tried to comfort me. Everything will be all right, he told me. But I cried out again and again that nothing would ever be all right. That was many years ago. Why is the memory returning now.

Tonight it is the nun who speaks to us. Every time there is mindfulness, we disempower what we are thinking or feeling, she tells us.

Metta Karuna means cherishing one's self as one cherishes a child. This body and this mind are our instruments for realization and so we must treat ourselves lovingly.

To sleep peacefully, sleep like the Buddha on the right side, right hand under the right cheek, left arm stretched out along the side.

Remember the refuge of the here and now against a flood of feelings or thoughts or confusions.

I walk back to my room beneath the bright stars. And then I sleep like the Buddha.

DAY 12

The end of the retreat is near. Only two more full days after today.

The monk suggests we might want to meditate outside this afternoon. So I splash upstream. Sheep startle out of the way as I approach. A heron lifts into flight. I find a sandbar in the sunlight and sit there.

In his evening talk, the monk speaks of Dependent Origination. During the first two hours of the night of Buddha's enlightenment, the monk explains, he understood how suffering arises. It is a concept I want to learn more about. The monk describes how our feelings become desire and then desire becomes grasping. It is when we can live at the level of feeling without desire that we can live in a harmonious way. He suggests that we watch this process happen, watch what pulls us away from pure mind.

I begin the sitting tonight feeling tired, sad. And yet when the bell sounds, I am not ready to end my meditation. I am beginning to realize how meaningful it would be for me to spend more time at the monastery.

DAY 13

Buddha allows only one desire, one attachment. That is the attachment to the practice of meditation.

I find a peacock feather lying in the meadow, its colors shimmering in the sunlight.

The monk speaks of bringing up disturbing patterns when we are calm and watching how they develop. Restraint arises, he says, from not wanting to hurt ourselves, like brakes on a car. It is mindfulness that stops the whole process of Dependent Origination.

He tells us about the old Thai master who was the teacher of the monks. Before he died, he was in a coma for many years. Shortly before he slipped into a coma, he would say puzzling things. Still and flowing water, he said. The mind is like still and flowing water. The phrase echoes within me.

It was about a year ago that I spent some time staying in the tiny villages along the Mekong river. I would sit on the bamboo porch of my guest hut above the river. The current was swift and unceasing. I watched the water sweep by and I watched my thoughts and feelings flowing endlessly past. It was Heraclitus who said that you cannot step twice into the same river. He also said there is nothing permanent except change. I sat beside the river of still and flowing water.

Day 14

This is the last full day of the retreat. The sun moves in and out of the clouds. I feel a deep peacefulness.

I sit by the stream awaiting the afternoon meditation session. I take off my shoes and cross the stream, feeling the coolness of the water. Peacocks cry from the treetops.

In the evening the monk speaks about the retreat that will end tomorrow and offers us parting advice. Remember to abandon the self, to relinquish the self, he tells us, and then you will have wholeness. It isn't necessary to plan. Allow for not knowing. Allow for uncertainty. It is possible to be happy, he assures us, to end our suffering. It truly is possible.

Day 15

During the last morning talk, the monk speaks of a conference he attended with the Dalai Lama. The Dalai Lama is always addressed as Your Holiness. And as the monk addressed him, he understood how literal the title was. He felt he was speaking to holiness itself.

When I say goodbye to the monk, he gazes into my eyes for a long time. And then I raise my hands to my forehead and bow my head.

Winning and Losing

I

It has been about a year and a half since my book of poems was accepted for publication by a small press. Last spring I got a call saying the book would come out in the summer. Now with only a few days of summer remaining, I am getting discouraged. I pick up the phone impulsively and call the publisher for news. If I thought about if for very long, I wouldn't call. I fear that maybe he has lost interest in the book or changed his mind.

The warmth of the publisher's voice eases my doubts. We have had only a few brief conversations by phone and have never met. He has also sent me a few handwritten cards and there was always a word or two that I puzzled over for hours. I have a surprise for you, he tells me now. He tells me the publication will be very special. The book has been selected to receive an important award. You must keep it a secret, he says, until the announcement in December.

He tells me that the committee of judges this year was unable to agree on a winner. He offered them my manuscript to consider and they all liked it. I'm not sure what else he says but it is something about reviews, a reading at a festival in Seattle next year, a gold seal on all the books. We will work together on the book in the next few months. I hang up the phone in a daze.

This summer has been a time of self doubt. Despite the appearance of my work in several magazines in the last few months, and a few acceptances from other publications, I found myself weary of the arduous process of sending out my writing. For the first time I began imagining not submitting my work anymore. It was only fantasy but it felt freeing.

I feel as though the conversation took place in a dream. The news seems wondrous and confusing. I am almost afraid to believe it. For the first time I perceive what a fine and perilous line might exist between reality and illusion. I hope I haven't crossed it. These dreamlike feelings are so new, so strange. I feel fragile and transparent.

I think about a conversation I had a few weeks ago with a friend who is a painter. She was longing for a show, longing for her paintings to receive more recognition. And I was talking of my own realization that recognition doesn't really help. It only awakens a fathomless desire. And yet to think of the award is daunting. It has fulfilled some desire that is deeper than mine ever dared to be.

In the days that follow, I say nothing about the news. I'm sure it would be all right to tell a few friends not involved in the writing world, to tell my children. My heart longs to call my parents who died years ago. They admired and saved all my publications and I think they talked proudly of me to their friends. And yet they had some dream, some image that reached beyond me that I could never fulfill.

I am living in a small cabin on an island in Puget Sound. I decide to pack a bag and travel to another island for a few days. I have been nursing a twenty-five year old cat with a hurt paw, not my cat but a neighbor's who has adopted me. For many days I have had to mix antibiotics in his food and to soak his paw in hot water, twice a day for fifteen minutes. He resisted but I think he knew I was helping him. He didn't struggle hard and mostly we sat quietly together on the

floor of a small travel trailer that serves as my bathroom and kitchen
. . . a brief morning and evening meditation. Now his paw has finally
healed and considering that and the news of the award, I am ready
for celebration. It is a warm day and I sit on the deck of the ferry
watching the deep green islands and the blue sea. I take a room in my
favorite inn and then wander around the town. In the window of the
bookstore I see a book with the dignified gold seal of the award. Of
course I've seen it before but never closely examined it. As I imagine
how my own book will look, that feeling of unreality sweeps over
me once more. What do you know about this award, I ask the
bookstore owner. Not much, she answers, only that the committee
is a small one and they often have difficulty reaching a decision.

As the days go by, I find I am treating myself more generously. I feel
more self respect. And I begin to write again after a silence of almost
a year. I imagine telling people the news, confiding it to them.
I think my friends will be glad for me. I know what jealousy is like,
both to feel it and receive it. But somehow I don't think that
will be anyone's response. The news is too extraordinary for that.
I wonder if others will mind that I waited so long to tell them when
they finally hear about the award. Am I lying by omission. And
yet I cherish this time of being alone with the knowledge, slowly
learning its shape and its feel. My first grandchild will be born soon
after the announcement. And this time of waiting is another gestation,
a time of carrying something new and precious within me.

My dreams become vivid. I dream my mother and I are alone and the
mood between us is a tender tryst. She is showing me a slim volume
of poems, her poems, that has just been published. We sit side by side
and look at the poems together. They are quiet and deep. One is about
a boat trip with my father. Another is about my brother as a boy.
There are gentle illustrations by an artist, pictures that appear almost
abstract but when we look closely there are many small lovely faces.

I never thought of my mother as a writer and yet now I think of a box of letters I have. In the year before her marriage, she wrote every day to my father. Each letter expresses her love and longing in such a captivating way that I have sometimes thought of publishing them.

I go on keeping my secret, talking to friends and saying nothing of the award. The concept of a secret awakens memories of childhood, of innocence. I can almost picture the diary I had as a girl with its tiny lock and key. On my birthday a few months ago, my children invited me to visit for a few days. I had the feeling something was afoot but they kept denying it. Soon after I arrived, we all began a journey. I wasn't allowed to know our destination. I pleaded for hints or clues but they wouldn't allow me any. Instead the journey unfolded before me, opening its bright petals one by one.

Before I spoke with the publisher, I had been planning to spend time this winter at a small Buddhist monastery. Now it seems even more important that I do this. The monks speak often of impermanence. Everything arises and ceases and is not self, they teach. And they speak of remembering this not only in times of pain, but also in times of joy.

I look up from my typewriter just as the sun is about to set behind the islands. The sky is cloudy but the Olympic Mountains in the distance are rimmed with light. I wonder at the words that have been pouring through me in the last few weeks. It was many years ago that I wrote the award-winning poems. Then too I had undergone a long period of silence, perhaps my longest. I think it had lasted several years. During times like this I have learned to trust that the silence is purposeful, that something is forming within me or something needs to be resolved. I always know the words will return. But oh their absence leaves an emptiness, a terrible void.

I had been living on the island for many years and felt it was time to go. I packed up everything I owned and gave away my cat to someone I knew would give her a good home. I gave up a wonderful waterfront cabin I had been renting for years. I drove down the coast slowly, stopping in many towns to look for a rental, to look around. I finally came to a halt after driving for about fifteen hundred miles. I hadn't found what I was looking for and didn't know what to do. I checked into a campground on the beach and set up a small dome-shaped tent. I read and took long walks. One evening at sunset I watched dolphins leaping into the air. In the evenings I built a small campfire and gazed at the flames. After a few weeks the weather began to turn chilly. I got in my car and began to drive north.

I reached a town finally and bought a newspaper and perused the ads. There was a room for rent at a Korean Zen monastery. I went to look at it and rented it for a few days. It was a bare room. I brought in a pad and sleeping bag, a pillow and a small battery operated lamp. It was enough. I sat by the river, allowing the peacefulness of the monastery to enter me. I meditated. One monk resided there and one evening he spoke to me. Who is watching, he asked me, and laughter bubbled through him. Who is it that is watching.

A few evenings later I telephoned a man on the island I had left. I told him where I was. I asked if he wanted to fly down and then drive back up the coast together. I had decided if he said no, I would remain at the monastery. He telephoned the next day to say he would come.

I said goodbye to the monk, knowing his question would stay within me. I met Mark at the airport and together we slowly traveled north. We walked long sandy beaches together, watching the waves flow in. We talked and drew close. I had loved this man for many years and for the first time it seemed possible that we might find a way to be together.

As we got further north, a day or two from the island, he grew very nervous. He knew he had to get home quickly but he didn't understand why. When we reached his home, he called his parents and learned his father had died. We held each other and cried together and in the morning he flew across the country to the funeral. We both knew he wouldn't be back for a long time.

The cabin I had left was still available. I built a fire and gazed out at the sea and the rain. The long northern winter had arrived and I was back in the place from which I had departed. I felt empty of feelings. I gazed at the sea and the rain and asked, Who am I. Who is watching. Now and then I had a fleeting glimpse of something mysteriously new. I surrendered deeply. There seemed nothing else to do.

A few nights later I woke up trembling. I sat up in the darkness and wondered what was happening to me. And then finally I fell asleep again. In the morning I sat down in front of my typewriter and wrote the first sixteen poems of a new manuscript. They flowed forth while I watched in wonder. The next day another seven or eight poems were written. The process left me filled with awe.

When I felt the outpouring was over, at least for a little while, I rode my bike around the island. After a few moments I had to stop at the small café to borrow a pencil and paper. For the poems kept arriving. When I wasn't writing new poems, I was working on the others, discarding parts, changing a word or a line. Driving to town a few days later, I had to keep pulling over to the side of the road to scribble quickly in a notepad. It took perhaps a few weeks for the poems to come to an end. The order was already determined for the poems seemed to emerge from one another. They seemed a gift from some unknown source. I felt humble and deeply grateful.

As the days go by the award still seems unreal. At times I am excited and my fantasies grow wild. I have submitted manuscripts here and there. I wonder if the publishers knew about the award, would they be more drawn to publish me. I wonder if I will be invited to give workshops and readings. The thought evokes excitement and also anxiety. I think about the book being reviewed and my first response is fear. And yet if the judging committee liked the manuscript, it is possible that reviewers might also like it. I apply for a grant and find myself imagining receiving it. And yet I know there will be enormous competition and I've always been convinced that my poems were too quiet to win a prize. I stopped entering the major competitions years ago, content with how sensible that decision was.

Once in the seventies someone made an astrological chart for me and then explained to me what it revealed. She said the second half of my life would be much easier than the first. She said I would receive a good deal of public attention. It sounded as if she were speaking of someone else.

I begin thinking about the possibility of building a small house on my land. I have two ten-by-twelve-foot cabins with wide windows looking at the sea. They each have a woodstove and one has electricity. And I have the small travel trailer. I bought the land about five years ago. The process of having trees felled and the land torn open to put in a well and septic system and electricity was very disturbing. I haven't been ready to even consider doing anything more.

My small cabins only allow me space for a few shelves of books. My files are under my bed. My manuscripts are in stacked file boxes on a shelf above my bed. Even my electric typewriter takes up too much room to leave out. It stands on the floor beside a small desk until I need it. I've been striving for simplicity and this way of living is only a few steps away from camping. I spend most of my time outdoors. A large firepit edged with rocks is really the heart of the land.

I like living this way but I am beginning to long for a study with a wide desk and my files and books in order all around me. The winters here are cold and rainy and a house would make living here easier. I wonder if the award is influencing my thinking, making me feel I deserve more. And yet I am aware that there would also be an enormous loss as well. I would be more insulated from the stars and the moon setting over the islands and the sound of the sea.

Autumn in the northwest comes suddenly. We are having a last few days of Indian summer and I decide to take a trip with a friend for a few days before the rains begin. It takes us a day to travel to Tofino, a small fishing village in British Columbia. I am deeply stirred by the dense virgin rain forests, by the coves and inlets and islands. Small Indian villages hug the shores. I go out in a boat to watch the gray whales at their feeding grounds, the huge bodies rising from the water and then diving into the deep.

I have brought what I am writing along with me. I needed a pause from it, a chance to look at it from a distance, to see it freshly. The geographic distance isn't necessary but I find it helps. It casts everything into a new light.

In Tofino I dream I am beginning a love affair, one that feels profound. Each time we meet, I tell my lover a different name. I am about to meet him once more and am filled with longing and tenderness. I realize it is time now to tell him my true name.

When I reach home again a monk from the monastery where I am planning to go this winter calls to arrange the dates with me. The monks will be on a three month retreat and I will be one of the lay people who come for awhile to assist in running the monastery. The monks will meditate from dawn until night. We will join them when we can.

I haven't spoken to him for about six months. It is a joy to hear his voice and to hear news of the monastic community. And just before we are ready to say goodbye, I find myself telling him about the award. *Mazel Tov,* he says, and the Yiddish words from a Buddhist monk make me laugh. How many people have you told, he asks me, and laughs when I tell him I haven't told anyone because I'm afraid it isn't true. He also writes and we have shared our writing through the years. He seems to understand all my feelings of delight and surprise and nervousness of the changes the award might cause in my life. He agrees it is just the right time for me to come to the monastery. I offer you *mudita,* he says. *Mudita* is a Pali word that is often translated as sympathetic joy. It is the antidote to jealousy, that quality of rejoicing in the good that befalls others.

When I hang up the phone, the award seems a little more real than it did before. I find myself growing afraid. There has been an easy flow to my life, moving from place to place and remaining as long as I want. I wonder if the award will present me with new responsibilities that will hinder my wanderings. I wonder if people will treat me differently. Will I begin to wonder if it is me they are fond of or some image of me that the award confers. What if it awakens a desire for more and more recognition. When the year ends and new winners are chosen, will I feel a great loss.

And yet deep below all the fears is a sense of peacefulness. I realize none of these things matter. My yearnings and fears and doubts flow by. I watch them arise and cease.

II

I go into town to do some errands and stop by the bookstore. They have a special display of prize-winning books. My eye is caught by a slim volume about the award I have won. It lists all the winners and finalists from the time the prize first originated. I buy the book and chat with the man behind the counter. He is excited about the book. He tells me he feels the award is the most prestigious in this country. I ride slowly home and as I wait for the ferry I read through the list of the poets who have won. I am certain I must have misunderstood or else I have slipped over into a world of delusion. It seems impossible that I could be so honored.

I call the publisher again. I have to. I ask him if this is truly happening. For a moment he pretends he has never heard of me and then he laughs gently and assures me that this is real. I tell him about finding the book on the winners of the prize and he agrees that it is a very impressive list. And then he asks me to look over my manuscript to see if there is a word or line I still want to change.

I begin thinking about how ill prepared I am. I haven't given a reading in years. And though I taught writing workshops for about twenty-five years, I haven't taught in the last few years. I have been living in remote villages in Washington and Northern California and the Greek islands, and haven't been in dialogue with other writers.

As I read over and over again the list of the past winners, I am swept again by waves of disbelief and awe. On an impulse I call my ex-husband. We've been talking by phone often lately and I've even told him I had a wonderful secret but I couldn't tell him yet. He has recently retired from teaching literature at a Midwestern university and I know he will share my wonder at the company I will soon be among. He does share my wonder, my sense of awe. We dream together about how others will respond, about the ways my life will change. But he keeps returning to a feeling that something is wrong. He asks again about the way my manuscript was given to the judging committee. He doesn't believe the award process could be that informal. Finally he tells me gently that there must be some mistake.

The next day I call the research librarians in a nearby city. I ask for any information they can find on the press and also the award. They mail their findings out to me the next day and I pour over them. The award process is quite formal and none of the dates my publisher has given me seem to jibe. And as I read the information on the press, I learn that they offer a prize with a very similar name. This must be the prize the publisher was referring to.

Tonight the wind is tossing all the fir branches. I leave the windows open. I dream the wind is blowing through me, cleansing me. And when I wake it is to a feeling of emptiness, a feeling of peacefulness. It is clear that the award was only a lovely dream. In the afternoon I wander down to the small island library. On the counter is a packet of gold seals. They are for a contest for the children of the island. Seeing them leaves me feeling very foolish.

I browse through the bookshelves and notice a new edition of the *I Ching,* a book I haven't thought about in many years. I surprise myself by checking it out. Back home again I review the instructions. And then I toss three coins to determine which hexagram I should read. Its title is "Adornment":

> Leaves the carriage and walks.
> It is in accordance with his position
> that he should not ride.

The humbleness it calls for seems fitting. And so does the hexagram it changes into. It is called The Mountain and counsels meditation and stillness.

The days become foggy and gray. I take long beach walks. The sea is as calm as a lake. The cat seems to be fading away. He can no longer follow me to the trailer at dinner time. Instead he just watches me go from his bed. I carry his bowl to him containing his favorite foods and he takes only a lick or two. He is growing slowly weaker. He seems peaceful and not in any pain.

I receive a card in the mail with a quote from Thich Nhat Hanh. Happiness is not an individual matter, it says. It seems a reminder. There has been far too much focus on myself these last few weeks. I think of my aunt who is in the hospital with an infection. I think of a lovely nun who suffered an aneurysm and may need surgery and of a friend whose niece is dying. I think of my grandchild preparing to be born in only a few months.

And still my thoughts sometimes return to the award. I feel strangely grateful for how much I have learned. For almost a month I was the winner of a major literary award. It could have been true. This happens to writers, a sudden honor that lifts them into fame. The experience felt complete with its lilting joy and excitement. And like a traveler returning from a journey to a faraway land, I feel deepened.

Yet even in my reveries about the award, I missed a simpler way of being. There is a feeling I have sometimes in Greece while walking for miles and miles down sunlit mountain roads with the blue sea gleaming below. The only way I can describe it is that I am flying. I know how to fly. But in these last weeks, I felt a weight on me, a new mantle of responsibility. It seemed my calendar would soon be filled with engagements. It seemed my life would grow more complex. I felt my wings being clipped.

I return to the present. I return to the here and now. I sit on the rug beside the woodstove. The cabin is lit with candlelight. The cat is curled in his bed outside the door. The night is still and a half moon is rising over the trees. This is enough, this is good enough, Ajahn Chah, a Thai Buddhist Master used to say. I have been feeling this so often since I realized I would not be receiving the award, a simple gratitude for all that I have.

Retreat

I stop in a small town as I approach the monastery. I have been feeling very peaceful about coming to spend six weeks at the monastery. But I am suddenly in a panic. I sit in a small café and sip a cup of coffee and try to relax. And then I drive on.

The beginning is gentle. I have a cup of tea with the ajahn. I was last here about a year ago and listen eagerly as he tells me about the past months. And then I move my things into the little trailer where I will live.

The monks are on a three month winter retreat. A visiting nun is also present. I am here along with a few other lay people to assist with the monastery chores. We prepare the meal which is served at 10:30 a.m. And at 5:00 p.m. we offer tea. Occasionally we run errands in town. The rest of the time we participate in the retreat, the sitting and walking meditation. Though now and then there is conversation, much of the time there is a deep and peaceful silence.

After tea one of the monks reads to us from a book about the Thai forest master Ajahn Mun. This is followed by a discussion. The retreat and the readings have been going on for about a month when I arrive, and I feel rather lost. The vocabulary of Pali words is unfamiliar and so are some of the concepts. Everyone seems to have traveled on far beyond me since I was last here.

The emphasis is on investigating the mind, employing *samadhi* or concentration. Not water buffalo *samadhi,* but using bright alertness to watch arising and ceasing, to investigate their origin.

—

The rains have set in, a steady warm rain. Fog drifts over the hills. The trees, half lost in mist, look as if they are making a pilgrimage to the mountaintops.

We meditate for an hour and then do walking meditation for an hour. There are a few covered walking paths. And if they are in use, we walk with an umbrella.

The reading today is about the need for effort, continuous effort. And the unimaginable bliss that is possible. The monk speaks of putting contentment into one's practice. And we speak of letting go of desire, the joy and freedom of that. To let go of desire and attachment is to have everything.

I have always had times in meditation when my legs are in a kind of agony, wanting to move, to keep moving. Shifting my position helps only for a moment. I have tried investigating the pain and it seems to increase unbearably. Ajahn Mun, the Thai master, writes of the *kilesas* or defilements that cause this. To enter into a deeper *samadhi* is a way to end this, he says.

When the hour for sitting meditation begins to seem endless, when I begin to become desperate for it to end, I imagine that I will be sitting for two or three hours. I let go of time. I surrender.

A young monk has decided to disrobe and will be leaving today. It was a very difficult decision for him but he seems at peace with it. He is fragile and beautiful in his uncertainty of what will come next. Everyone is sad to see him go.

I am learning new Pali words:

> *Citta* – the mind
> The *Kilesas* – those demons within us that we must
> summon the energy to deal with.

There is a great deal of talk about the constant striving that is needed and the joy and strength that it brings. I begin to catch glimpses of the calm and purity of the mind and watch all the disturbances within me that arise and cease.

Rain and more rain. The ground is saturated. So are the trees and the grass and the sky. Spring bulbs poke from the ground. There is a brown towhee on my walking path. It doesn't fly away as I walk slowly back and forth.

The rice that is left from the meal is put out on the back porch each day. The birds seem to wait for it. Scrub jays, acorn woodpeckers with their bright red fluffy caps, tiny tufted titmice and towhees.

My son and his wife are having a baby. I talk to them every few days. The baby is almost two weeks overdue and the doctors are considering inducing labor. The ajahn often asks about them. Tonight the monks do a special long chant in Pali for a healthy birth.

My little granddaughter has been born. Someone tells me there is a message on the answering machine about her birth. The telephone at the monastery isn't working because of a wild rainstorm. I jump in the car in the rain and darkness to look for a phone in the valley. A kind man at a gas station lets me use his phone. My son sounds very sweet and moved by his new little daughter. And his wife tells me they both cried as they watched the birth. When I return to the monastery, the monks seem pleased with the news.

I would like to ask if they would chant for the new baby, but I feel shy about it. Just as the evening chanting is about to begin, the ajahn asks me the name of my new granddaughter. And they chant a long and beautiful chant for her. I feel grateful to the monks and grateful for my life which allows me to be here at the monastery listening to the chanting that is welcoming my granddaughter into this life.

Today after tea the ajahn continues with his readings. He describes a Thai monk and his experiences of fearlessly confronting cobras and tigers during his stay in the Thai jungles. He was warned against meditating in a certain cave where a very fierce cobra lived. He explained that it would create bad karma to allow fear to stop him. During the discussion I ask about this. Fear would indicate not trusting his own karma, even if it brought about his death, the ajahn explains to me. And to present the enemy with fear invokes violence. And thus one becomes responsible for the karma of one's attacker. In these perilous situations the monks meditate deeply on the word *Buddho* or enter a deep state of *metta* or loving-kindness. The ajahn describes his own encounter with a cobra as he slept in a mosquito net in the jungle. The cobra touched his head and moved back and forth before him. Finally it slid peacefully away.

He tells of a rather strange monk who decided he wanted to walk through a herd of wild elephants while concentrating on *metta*. He emerged unharmed.

I ask the ajahn if he isn't bored here in California. He laughs and responds, "It is the people here that are interesting."

I am fascinated by his tales of roaming the Thai forests filled with tigers, pythons, elephants and cobras, by the monks who set up their mosquito umbrellas alone in the jungles to meditate in solitude.

⌒

Last night's meditation was very deep even from the start. I came a little early and wasn't aware of others arriving and the opening candle lighting and bows. At the end of the hour I didn't hear the bell nor understand why everyone seemed to keep moving around. I opened my eyes reluctantly to find that the hour had ended.

The ajahn's talk was about effort, about enlightenment being attainable. All our excuses (too young, too old, too sick) are only *kilesas*.

Tonight we meditate until midnight. It has gotten very cold and very clear. In the morning and evening the temperature is about twenty degrees. I like bundling up in a coat and blanket and walking back and forth on the meditation path beneath the shimmering stars.

⌒

I drive into town to do some errands. I buy a book that one of the monks has been wanting. And I take the monastery mail to the post office. I buy a few things that are needed at the store. I find even this small town overwhelming. I stop in a café for coffee and the noise seems deafening. I look at the front page of a newspaper and it makes me dizzy. I hurry back to my walking path and my meditation cushion. I hurry home to the silence.

My workload this week was very light. Next week I will be helping to prepare the meal each day. Seeing the new list of chores takes me aback for a moment but I know it will be fine. I will be preparing tea for the first time. There are many small details to learn. At even the smallest setback part of me is ready to flee. But being here feels like a precious opportunity. By committing myself for all these weeks, I find myself again and again surrendering to the teaching.

Today I keep thinking of a book I read years ago about a pilgrim who wanted to learn to pray continuously. I find when I finally lie down at night that I am still meditating, still watching my breath. I get confused about how in the world I will ever sleep, but then I just do.

⌒

I have a beautiful interview with one of the ajahns. He has been a friend and teacher for many years. I describe my meditation experiences to him. And I talk to him about *The Way of the Pilgrim*. He has read it and smiles when I tell him I want to learn to meditate unceasingly.

Since I've been here my meditation has changed to a simple watching of the breath. And sometimes it grows so fine, I can no longer distinguish between the in breath and the out. I have shared all this at the interview and it leaves me joyous. And even though it is long past bedtime I feel wide awake. I feel as if I have shared my deepest secrets with someone who completely understands. I feel such gratitude to this monk, such trust that he will guide me wisely.

My former husband calls me. He is in deep pain. He has recently retired and his teenage son has left home for the first time. And, of course, he is also a new grandfather. He is having intense and debilitating anxiety attacks. I am worried about him but I have the feeling he is about to break into a new and exciting time of life. He seems soothed by my words.

My new granddaughter cries a lot. I can hear her sweet cries on the phone and they make me long to hold her, to comfort her. My son sounds lost in love, rocking her and singing to her to ease her entry into this world. What a beautiful father he will be.

I drive down to the valley every few days to make calls. It seems important to stay in touch at this special time. I have been on ten-day meditation retreats and held my life at bay. But I like this weaving together of the different parts of my life. I am even having my mail forwarded to me once a week. My meditation doesn't feel interrupted. Instead it feels richer and wider.

~

And still the sitting periods aren't easy. My knees ache and so does my back. Sometimes I feel a deep reluctance. Yet there is a radiance when I meditate and sometimes I wonder if it hasn't been there for a long time. I remember meditating in Greece a few years ago, sitting on my bed or on the rooftop terrace of a beautiful house I rented, listening to the village clock chime out the half hour and the hour.

In only a few more days, the meditation schedule will be suspended and we will do individual retreats for awhile. I hope I will still find the discipline for long meditation. I hope the time doesn't hang heavy and fill me with restlessness. Simple distractions like wandering into the kitchen for a snack aren't possible here. Reading anything but Buddhist literature seems out of reach. The mind becomes too refined for that.

~

I am grateful so often that I have come for an extended period of time. The departure date is too far away to fantasize about. I feel flung into the present, into surrender at being here.

I am learning to feel comfortable cooking for about fifteen people, judging amounts needed. I always cook with someone else but am beginning to trust my own judgment. And I have almost mastered all the details of serving the afternoon tea.

At 5:00 a.m. when I rise it is twenty degrees. By 7:00 a.m. it grows light. Now it is a few hours later and the sun has climbed over the hills and sheds its warmth.

The clouds today look like thick white fleece, a flock of celestial lambs moving across the sky. I am wrapped in a blanket, walking back and forth on the path. I watch flickers of restlessness arise. I watch my thoughts fly to the future and to the past. Then I return to the feel of my breath, to the crunch of pebbles beneath my feet.

Wonderful photos arrive of the new baby. I can barely see her but I can see the expression of tenderness on my son's face. And I talk again to my ex-husband and he is doing much better.

Today many of the monks are away for the day. I speak to one of the young monks about my frustration that my peaceful meditations don't seem to change me during the time I am not meditating. I find myself easily annoyed and lacking in loving kindness. He tells me concentration isn't the end we are seeking. Instead it prepares the way for investigation and contemplation. It is from these that wisdom and joy arise. My mood lifts after the conversation. Perhaps it is his words or is it that speaking about my feelings allows me to no longer feel so alone with them.

In the afternoons I have been walking up the steep monastery road. At the top there are wonderful paths through the woods. Today I visit the waterfall and watch the clear water flowing effortlessly down.

Tonight the stars fill the sky, cascading down to the hilltops. It is hard to shut my door and climb into bed. I feel like I am shutting them away.

A puppy appears at the monastery. His fur is golden brown, the shade of the monks' robes. All afternoon he walks beside me on the walking path. But the monks insist they don't want a dog at the monastery. Someone suggests he may live at a Russian Orthodox monastery up the road a mile or so. The nun and I create a leash from a piece of twine and climb up to the monastery. It is a lovely place with domed buildings overlooking a pond. A bearded monk greets us warmly but the dog isn't one of theirs.

I cherish my walk and my visit with the nun. I have stayed at her monastery in England, and ask for news of the nuns that I know. And she tells me of a monk in Australia who leads groups to the sacred places of India. How I would love to join one of his groups.

When we return we see that a sign about the dog has been placed on the road. Toward evening his owner drives up to claim him.

One of the ajahns is away for a few days. He was asked to act as the spiritual advisor for a man who is scheduled to be executed. At the evening meditation the monks chant for the prisoner. And there is a talk about loving kindness and about how we are all one. The Buddha says even the people who are using a two-man saw to cut us into pieces should receive our loving kindness. Not their *kilesas* or defilements but their *citta* or heart.

I wish I could take notes to capture each word of the talk, the precision and the poetry. Instead I listen deeply. One of our afternoon readings was about meditating during the talks, allowing them to enter us.

Today is gray, the streams filled with rushing water from all the rain. And I feel gray, uninspired and half wishing I could leave. I need to contemplate surrender, relinquishment. There is too much I am hanging onto.

I climb up again to the waterfall. We have had many days of rain and it is much fuller than before. On the path back I see a large jack rabbit with long legs and very long ears. It allows me to get very close. It looks like an illustration from a children's book.

Today there is hail and sleet and snow. Quick downpours with the sun still shining. Now everything is sprinkled with snow.

As we are having tea, the ajahn returns from his stay with the prisoner. The man was executed last night at 12:01. The ajahn sits with us and describes his moving experience. The prisoner was Thai, a man named Jay, who was very loved by the prisoners and even the guards. Many years earlier in Thailand he had been ordained as a monk for three months and recently had returned to his Buddhist practice. His meditation was filled with light. He was very grateful for the presence of the ajahn who stayed beside him for his last few days. As the time for the execution drew nearer, the ajahn warned him against depleting his energy with all the visitors crowded around him. And at the end he suggested that he let go of his breath and concentrate only on the light.

Jay had been present at a robbery in which two people had been killed. He was convicted for the killings though he claimed he hadn't known they would happen and was trying to prevent them. But he refused to provide the name of the killer. He had spent many years in prison and earned the love of many people. Two former jurors wanted him released. The pope as well as a former prison warden made pleas for clemency. But the stay of execution was refused. The execution took place while hundreds of people held a vigil outside the prison gates in a wild wind and rainstorm. The ajahn visited the funeral home the next day and viewed the body. The expression on Jay's face was deeply peaceful.

I have an interview with the ajahn. I talk to him about how dismayed I am that my state of mind seems so ordinary. I somehow expected the deep meditation to enhance everything. I hoped to feel uplifted or full of brightness. He says that there are times when he also feels this way. But even at these times he is aware of subtle changes—letting things go more easily, being a bit more present for whatever is needed. I do not talk to him about how hard I am finding it to be living in a community, how much resistance I feel. Most of the time I live alone and I am finding the change difficult. But I feel I can work on this on my own.

Tonight in meditation, I find myself contemplating the Eight Worldly Conditions:

Praise and Blame
Happiness and Suffering
Honor and Dishonor
Gain and Loss

To see things in this way reduces everything to simplicity. I felt as if my meditation had been guiding me to this investigation. It felt deeper and clearer than ordinary thinking.

⁓

There is so much said at the discussion periods that I want to ponder. One of the ajahns makes the statement that in the Buddhist view, things are preconditioned rather than predetermined. And he also speaks of the practice of sharing merit, dedicating any goodness that might arise from our actions to others.

Yesterday the talk was about declaring one's attainments. A monk is not permitted to announce that he is enlightened. Many years ago a Thai monk kept claiming that another monk was an *arahant,* an enlightened being. A lot of divisiveness resulted at the monastery. The abbot asked the monk himself to make a statement. The monk responded quietly that he hadn't seen any *kilesas* arise in seven years and that his life was like turning the pages of a book and that every page was blank.

There is more discussion of investigation and I begin to feel confident that I understand. It is a process of considering whatever arises in the light of Buddhist teachings. I think of my contemplation of the Eight Worldly Conditions. Seeing everything as one of these conditions provides an opportunity to learn non-attachment, to let go of joy or suffering. There was a formality and dignity that felt new to me. I feel I have been provided with a precious tool.

The nun speaks of how difficult it is for her sometimes to focus on her breath. It makes me realize I am lucky that this method works for me. The monks also speak of how it is necessary now and then to change the meditation object. It can grow stale or dull eventually. I think I knew this intuitively and perhaps it is even why I am drawn to the monastery at certain times.

The discussions burn through some of my stubborn resistance. I feel more present, more alert. Brighter.

The readings from the Thai master continue and the discussion is often about monastic life in Thailand. There are Thai monks with psychic powers who can see what realm one will be reborn into. The monks talk of the superstition that exists in the Thai culture. The people sometimes come to a talk at the monastery in the hope that somewhere in the talk a number will be mentioned. They believe any such number will come up in the lottery.

And there is talk of the cremations of the great teachers. Their relics or remains are found to be crystalline or opalescent. And there have been great masters whose bodies after death show no signs of decomposition. The ajahn says that the time they have spent in *samadhi* or deep concentration has changed the body's chemistry.

I dream my father is dying. I am talking to someone who says to me how hard this must be for me. My response is to break into sobbing. My father died ten years ago and I have never sobbed like this.

I wonder if the dream was evoked by the birth of my grandchild. The birth has stirred so many memories. I think of the joyous arrival of my own children. And I remember that my own grandmother died the day I was born. What a chaos of emotion my mother must have felt. I think often of my mother and father who didn't live long enough to see their great grandchild. How I would have loved to call them with the news.

⁓

Tonight the ajahn gives a talk and tells us more about his time with Jay. There is a special chant in Pali that is used to request that a monk give a talk. Jay remembered the chant. The ajahn asked if he remembered the meaning of the request. He went on to explain that Buddha after his enlightenment had not wanted to teach. He was swayed by a Brahma god who told him there were those with only a little dust in their eyes who would hear him. As he spoke he noticed that not only was Jay listening earnestly but so were the guards.

The two chanted together and meditated and talked. The ajahn had been warned that the guards might be rude and hostile. But instead they passed notes to each other to communicate. And when one of them spoke too loudly, the others asked him to be quiet. Jay is talking with the monk now, they explained.

Jay had studied painting in prison and an exhibition of his paintings was being shown at the Oakland Museum at the time of his execution.

⁓

My stay is almost over. Only a week or so remains. It is hard to imagine leaving. It is tea time now. One monk is darning his thick wool socks. A lay woman is crocheting. The nun sits in stillness and silence. People take turns rising to pour themselves a second cup of tea.

I stand for a few moments in the kitchen and watch the birds on the little back porch. There is a towhee that comes for the crumbs each day that has no long tail feathers. And yet it seems healthy and active. It can fly and its balance doesn't seem to be impaired. The acorn woodpeckers are the clowns of the group. They call loudly and flit back and forth. It is hard to watch them without smiling.

I walk back and forth on the meditation path. For a few moments there is warm sun like a caress. Then rain again, this peaceful steady rain.

Tonight there is an all night sitting. In the midnight talk the monk speaks of the silence of the heart as a refuge, of taking *no self* as a refuge, of taking relinquishment as a refuge.

I listen to a tape of a talk by one of the ajahns entitled "My Life as a Monk." In it he speaks a great deal about the desert one crosses in meditation. When I am not feeling inspired, I feel I should leave, that I don't belong. I begin to realize how cruel this is to myself. Instead I need to realize that this submission to monastic life can be difficult. It involves a stripping away. This is only a time of resistance that I am going through.

I drive into the valley to buy supplies for hot fudge sundaes for the community. Another lay person and I will be leaving and want to present the sundaes as *dana,* as our offering after the meal. I buy ice cream, fudge syrup, caramel, nuts and bananas for toppings. I think the young monks especially will be pleased by such an unexpected treat.

This morning I meditated for two hours without interruption. And yet I still feel a great deal of sadness and resistance. I have an interview with the ajahn this afternoon and for the first time I am reluctant. I am ashamed of whatever I might say.

But of course the talk with the monk turns out to be wonderful. I confess feeling like an impostor any time I don't feel radiant or am not meditating well. He laughs in response. We all feel that way sometimes, he tells me. He goes on to talk of the impasses we all face and I promise myself to remember this.

The monastery is allowing a few people to take temporary ordination for two or three months. Now I talk to the ajahn about perhaps doing that sometime. I feel I would learn so much, learn to work my way through impasses and resistance. It would be an opportunity to deepen the teachings within me.

The ajahn speaks to me of the difference between waiting and patience. Waiting is an absurd state because it doesn't allow the present. It doesn't allow mindfulness. I want to remember this for it seems I have spent so much of my life waiting. Patience, on the other hand, allows one to rest contentedly in the moment.

My talk with the ajahn leaves me filled with joy. I tell one of the younger monks about our talk of feeling like an impostor. He laughs and agrees that he certainly sometimes feels like that. That is why we need *sangha,* the community of Buddhists, he goes on to say.

～

We serve the sundaes after the meal. One of the ajahns is British and has never tasted a sundae before. The huge bowls of ice cream are passed around and are now completely empty. Everything that arises, ceases.

⌒

My last day at the monastery. My thoughts fly forward to a long visit with my new granddaughter. And they sweep backward contemplating what a rich and special time this has been. There is so much I will take away with me, so many teachings to contemplate and meditate on. I feel they are waiting to slowly unfold within me. And then I return to the present, to this bright sunshine after many days of rain. I walk down the path to sit beside the rushing stream and watch the water flowing swiftly by. And then I walk back to the meditation hall.

Today is *Magha Puja,* a celebration of the full moon of February when 1,250 *arahants* spontaneously gathered around the Buddha. People are beginning to arrive for the celebration and the evening talk. At midnight we will circumambulate the meditation hall carrying incense and candles and flowers.

I enter the meditation hall and bow three times. And then I sit down and meditate.

Call of the Loons

It is New Year's Day and I am about to read the journal I have written during the past year. This has become a ritual I carry out each year. For a little while as I read, time seems to be held in abeyance. I feel I am out at sea in a rowboat during a slack tide, that pause between the tides when the sea ceases its unrelenting pull. I stow my oars and the boat floats gently in place.

The writing book is unlined. The cover is of cloth, striped with soft colors. Inside are many loose papers. A leaflet on manta rays. Small pages covered with scribbled notes I meant to include when I found the time. A warm telephone message from my brother.

The year starts out at a Buddhist monastery. I was one of a few lay people helping out during a monastic retreat. I skim over that section quickly. I have written a story drawn from those pages and the words are too familiar to want to read them again. Except for sometimes using parts of the journal for stories or essays, I read it only once at the end of the year. There are surprises here and there . . . nothing I've truly forgotten, but events I haven't thought of since they occurred.

I begin reading about the long drive I took after leaving the monastery, a slow trip from Northern California to Washington. I read of the wild winds and rain, of the elk standing beside the road. I pulled over to the shoulder and got out of the car. The elk were only a few feet away and no fence separated us:

Massive and proud they watch me and a few other people that
have gathered. The horned males gaze at us challengingly. I
am sure if I stepped forward, they would charge.

And I read of stopping at a coastal motel on a hill in a wind so fierce
I am afraid to open the door of the car. And driving the next day
beside the ocean and suddenly coming upon the New Clarissa, the
oil tanker that had caused a massive oil spill on the pristine Oregon
beaches:

> It looms offshore suddenly like a specter—dark and ghostlike
> and battered. It had been towed thirty miles offshore with
> special cable but broke free in the storm last night and floated
> back to shore. The highway has come to a halt with everyone
> parked on the shoulders. I follow some others through the
> thick wet salal to a viewpoint at the edge of a bluff.

I had forgotten the exhilaration of the stormy journey, the long
detours and flooded roads, the areas covered with snow. I come to
a passage describing a stay in Newport:

> I go down to the harbor where the sea lions are barking and
> having territorial standoffs on the dock. I battle the wind
> and take a long beach walk.
>
> The area I stay in has many shops and bookstores and cafés. I
> seem to want to buy everything I see. I do buy a woolly hat, a
> fountain pen, a new journal. I luxuriate in a feeling of freedom,
> of no longer needing to adhere to the strict monastic
> schedule. And I keep wondering if it was my long stay at the
> monastery that leaves me feeling so strong and clear.

The journal is a literary form that I often seek out to read. And for
many years I taught correspondence courses in journal writing for

a university. Many of my students lived in remote areas and wrote of solitude, of islands and rocky beaches, of walks in the woods. I found many of their passages moving. And now as I reread my own journal, I am moved that I was the one driving that wild stormy coast.

I sometimes feel a twinge of envy when I read a journal, even my own. It is the feeling of bare attention, of pure presence in the moment that awakens it. I go on turning the pages of my journal. As I read, I get a glimpse of a fragment of my life, a shard I can hold up to the light.

I come to passages about finally reaching home, a small piece of land I own on an island near Canada:

> The first few days are traumatic ones when nothing seems to work. The land is strewn with fallen branches. This afternoon I gather some and make a bonfire. Warmed by its flames, I watch the sun sink into the sea.

And a few days later I write:

> Clearing my land of a million branches that blew down during the winter. Heaps everywhere waiting to be burned. This is a work day. I make piles of brush, clean out the firepit, cut kindling for the woodstove, fix the bird feeder and the shed door. As the light begins to fade, I sit in the cabin by the fire, tired and content.

As I continue through the journal I find many passages reflecting on my stay at the monastery. It is the first time I have left there feeling an eagerness to be gone. I felt certain that my deep connection to Buddhism was still intact and yet I worried about how restless I had felt toward the end of my stay:

I have never felt this resistance to the monastery before. I think now I was overwhelmed by my time there. Perhaps this pulling back is in response to having allowed all the teachings to enter me deeply. A panic in response.

. . . I realize tonight that my pulling back from Buddhism is because I glimpsed the vastness of the surrender, the relinquishment that is required. How can it be so much vaster than I knew. Our readings of the great Thai masters with their one-pointed path, their deep seriousness, has revealed something deeper than I knew. I feel poised on some brink. I think of the way I enter a sea to swim. I move forward one step at a time. And in between each step, I stand motionless for a long time.

The next section of the journal is about a trip I took to the island of Hawaii. I was visiting with a friend there for a few weeks. I had been on the island once before and found it mysterious and lovely and a little frightening:

Rain and clouds and sun. Mockingbirds and cardinals and iguanas. What a strange and beautiful place.

We stay for a few nights at a resort in Kona. In the evening we sit on the wide terrace beside the sea. The lights on the water draw the manta rays here each night to feed on the plankton. The manta rays seem to fly through the water, lifting their rays above the sea. They are silvery white on the underside. Their dark mysterious shapes glide in wide slow circles. It is hard to pull myself away to finally go inside to sleep.

I found the beauty of Hawaii enchanting. I'm surprised I didn't write more in the journal. Perhaps because I wasn't alone very often, there wasn't time for quiet contemplation. On the way home I had a long layover at the Honolulu airport and sat writing in the lovely garden there. It was a last attempt to capture the images of the island before the immediacy was lost:

> I have written so little of these days and nights. Naalehu, where a wild cold wind seems to blow relentlessly. Our visits to the black sand beach where we would lie on the sand between the sea and the lagoon. Coconut trees towering over our heads. And usually one large and wonderful sea turtle could be found sleeping on the sand nearby until the incoming tide would sweep it back into the sea.

Journal writing has its own rhythm. There are times when I write nothing in the journal for months. This could be a period when I am doing other writing or simply a period of not writing at all. I notice that when I feel troubled I don't write very often. But when I do, the journal helps me to find my way. At times of joy, I turn to the journal eagerly, the words flowing, dancing from my pen.

I return to my land. For a long time now I have been struggling with the decision of whether or not I should sell the property. There are problems with neighbors, with roving sheep that consume anything I try to grow. And a fierce prevailing southwest wind sweeps the land in winter sometimes toppling the tall firs. I cherish the peacefulness, the solitude, yet after months of isolation, I begin to feel swallowed by it. And even then its beauty holds me captive. Again and again I chronicle its magic:

> Yesterday I saw a large and very beautiful otter in the meadow grass near the cabin. Such graceful curves. I watch it disappear over the bluff. I suspect it climbed up to search for a nesting place.

And tonight there are seven band-tailed pigeons at the feeder. It sways wildly with their weight. They are so crowded together there that one pigeon rests briefly on the upraised tail of another until it can finally wedge itself among the others.

Such warm lovely days. Today is the lowest tide of the year and lowest in many years. −3.5, the tidebook says. I splash along the exposed sand bank. Clams with their strange heads poked above the sand. Many brightly colored starfish lie exposed. Three bald eagles are perched on the rocks and lift into graceful flight as I approach.

And I come upon an entry about a mysterious experience I had forgotten:

This afternoon at the beach there is no wind and the sea is perfectly still. I hear a low melodic hum from the sea that mystifies me. I have never heard it before. Then far off in the distance I see the spouting of a whale. Its back rises from the water and then its tail. And tonight at sunset I hear the sound again. And again in the distance I see the spout of a gray whale. They are rarely present in this inland sea. I have heard that gray whales have a song. I wonder if that might be what I am hearing. The sound is deep and mesmerizing, almost like a chant.

I come to the end of this writing book and turn to the next. The only enclosures in this one are many four-leaf clovers pressed between its pages. I found them on my daily walks around the island. On a page near the back I have listed the names of the monks at the monastery. New monks often arrive and their names are unfamiliar ones in Pali. And on the last page is a list of the books that I especially enjoyed reading.

The entries begin with the finding of a four-leaf clover:

> Walking along the road, I suddenly realize I have just seen a four-leaf clover. I retrace my steps and find that it is truly there. It has been years since I last found one. It feels like this one found me for my thoughts had been far away. I hope it is a good omen.

The journal also begins with a decision to put my land up for sale:

> The ad for my land is in the newspaper today. So far there have been no calls. But I feel lighter, almost freed from the dark mood that has hovered over me. The world begins to fill with new possibilities.

> And meanwhile I feel grateful to be here, watching the sea and the almost continuous flow of birds at the feeder—pine siskins, purple finches and today for a sunlit moment a bright goldfinch. A solitary black-headed grossbeak. Band-tailed pigeons who startle into their rustling flight.

> Just now the sky is turning a deep pink and crimson streaked with lilac. The sea is a misty ethereal blue.

Writing in the journal helped during this time of uncertainty. As I wrote I was able to simply watch the swings of feeling arise and cease. The writing was a reminder of the Buddhist teachings about impermanence, about letting go:

> My first call in response to my ad came this evening. I feel rushes of fear, of sadness. I try to keep returning to mindfulness.

As I continue turning the pages of the journal I come to passages about visiting with my son and his wife and my new granddaughter. She was born while I was at the monastery and I left for a week to see her and welcome her into the world. The evening she was born, the monks did a long chant in Pali for her:

> She is four months old now. Each time I see her, she grows more responsive. Now she smiles as I play peek-a-boo with her. She has learned to turn over. And she coos, plays with sounds. Some are sweet and melodious and others are startlingly loud.

I am moved by what a new relationship this is. It defines itself so slowly. It is confusing at first to have my motherly instincts reawakening, that deep well of feelings. Confusing because this is not my baby, not motherhood, but something else. A new and tender connection that will gradually shape itself.

It is summer now and the land is enchanting. The sunsets hold me spellbound:

> Tonight the whole sky is a rainbow of colors. Looking up through the trees, there are bands of orange shading into pinks. And near the sea are streaks of golden light.

As I read I have to be careful not to crush the fragile four-leaf clovers I keep finding between the pages:

> Today I find a cluster of four-leaf clovers. They often grow in groups. I pick some and stop at a friend's house to give one to her. And then a few days later, I find many more. I don't want to pick any more. Maybe others will find them. There is joy enough in seeing them.

I swing from sadness and deep confusion about the land to imagining all the places I might live if I find a buyer. And through it all I experience my love of this place:

> Tonight I take a pillow and a fleece blanket and lie in the glider. As the sunset fades the sky turns a deep blue-green. The northern twilight lingers on and on and the sea is utterly still.

I begin painting watercolors of my favorite spots. One is of the hill behind my cabin where large rocks are surrounded by graceful meadow grass. Another shows the wide cabin deck and the sea just beyond.

There has been little response to my private ad about the land and now I list it with a realtor. I am honest with her about how torn I feel. It seems important for her to know I might change my mind. She seems very understanding.

It is my birthday and I decide to spend a few days in Victoria. I seem to drop my cares when I travel. There is a passenger boat that departs each morning from the mainland. The boat is small and the ride is a lovely one, weaving among the islands. The captain points out eagles perched at the tops of trees. And we spend awhile following a pod of orcas:

> The Bed and Breakfast where I stay is charming. The owner serves me tea and cookies when I arrive. And then I wander the neighborhood with its simple cottages and overflowing gardens. I walk along the waterfront stopping to listen to a group of Andean musicians and watch the street artists draw remarkable portraits.

I feel I have been granted a reprieve. Could my long period
of indecision be ending. I was beginning to feel I would
become ill if I stayed in that state much longer.

At the art museum, there is an exhibit of the paintings of Emily
Carr. I have seen some of her paintings. And read many of her
books. She writes with such warmth, such honesty of her struggle
to paint, her surprise at even the simplest recognition of her art. I
have grown very fond of her from my reading. This exhibit has a
few paintings that I've never seen:

> I hadn't known her style evolved into these soaring visions.
> I gaze for a long time at her lone tree against the sky, her
> painting of a huge sky above the sea. My heart leaps at
> seeing them.

Back home again I go on painting pictures of my land. I have very
little skill but these paintings feel necessary, a way of paying tribute
to its beauty, a way of saying thank you. I wonder if this is also my
way of saying goodbye:

> The paintings are teaching me how gentle the colors are
> here. I have painted a little in Greece—those gleaming
> dancing blues of the sea and sky. Here the islands are a deep
> gray that shifts to mossy green or a misty blue-gray. And the
> sea is more silver than blue.

> This afternoon I sit at the picnic table, filled with longing to
> paint the yew tree's graceful branches and the cabin. It seems
> impossibly hard but I finally convince myself to try. A few
> hours later the painting is done. The perspective isn't right
> and the yew tree looks more like a willow but the love is there
> that I was yearning to express. It seems almost a miracle that I
> have the images, the colors before me now in the sketchbook.

The end of summer is approaching and I begin to make plans to return to northern California. The winters on the island are long and dark and lonely. And yet even as I begin to think about leaving, I am haunted by the beauty:

> I wake to the calling of loons . . . not separate calls but two
> loons weaving their plaintive lovely notes together. Deep
> fog drifts over the islands, over the tall majestic firs. The sea
> gradually disappears.

There are gaps of a few weeks now between the journal entries. There is a brief description of a visit from a friend. And then I write of a decision not to sell the land, at least for now:

> I get an offer on the land but it is a very low one with
> complicated terms. I take the property off the market.

> I have felt so tormented by what to do. I have decided to
> wait until I feel clear, until the whole process can be more
> gentle, more graceful.

I think I write so little because the subject is fraught with feeling. All summer I have been saying goodbye, I've been letting the land go. If in my wanderings I find a place I want to buy, I think I will be able to relinquish this one without too much more pain. But the future seems so unknown. Perhaps the land will be mine for a long time to come.

There is another visit from my granddaughter just before I depart:

> Lazing on the cabin bed with the baby beside me. I tickle
> her and listen to her sweet laughter. And then I hold her
> close to me, feeling her dear baby solidness.

And I write of other young visitors:

> I look up seeing a flurry of activity at the feeder. A black-headed grossbeak is feeding its baby whose tail quivers wildly each time a seed is placed in its mouth. And now an assortment of birds come to feed. Nuthatches, towhees, and Steller's jays. An unfamiliar bird appears that I suspect is a baby. The young have a special blurry look about them. It turns out to be a baby purple finch. I watch its wings flicker in excitement as its mother feeds it.

There is a pause of a month or so before the journal writing begins again. I am living in northern California, in a seaside town where I have lived many times. I am still there now. I skim very quickly through the remaining pages. The passages feel too familiar, too close in time to engage my interest. Only one entry captures my eye:

> Just outside my house I find a bird's nest. It is lying in the middle of the road, blown down by the wind. It must be a nest from last summer. Lying within it is a tiny gray and white speckled egg that is still intact. The nest is finely woven. It seems impossible that a small bird was able to create it.

As I look up from reading I can see the nest on my kitchen window sill where I placed it. And then I look beyond it. The winter light is quickly fading. It is time to return to the present, time to return to this new year that has barely begun. I grab a coat and scarf and walk toward the sea. I want to catch a glimpse of it before it grows dark.

Walking the Footpath
of the Buddha

Toward the end of meditation retreats the question frequently arises of how to continue practicing in daily life. I am a traveler, spending long periods of time in Greece, a country that captured my heart many years ago. On these small Greek islands I often find myself contemplating how my travel can be part of the practice even though I am far from the Buddhist monastery I often visit. The time alone seems an opportunity for me to absorb some of the teachings I have received, a chance for me to begin to enact them.

It is summer and I rent a little house away from the sea. All the seaside villages are filled now with holiday travelers, with music and cars and motorbikes. Because my house is deep inside an inland village where the tourists seldom venture, I am hoping to find quiet.

I quickly discover that the house is far from silent. It is surrounded by a cluster of houses that face each other around a small plot of ground. My Greek neighbors cluster on their verandas talking loudly until deep into the night. Roosters crow and donkeys bray. Dogs bark and babies cry. Groups of children play and call to one another in shrill voices.

Each evening I carry my pillow to the far side of the house seeking a quieter and more private place. Here fields stretch away before me and a yellow moon floats in the sky. Still the sounds of the village life go on, voices from a distant group of houses carrying across the fields. Just below me a pump groans on and off. I sit and meditate listening to the sounds that come and go and listening to the silence. It is there beyond the calling of children and beyond the donkey's poignant bray. It is there between the gusts of wind that sweep through the olive trees.

I contemplate the stripping away that travel entails. I usually rent a simple room furnished with two beds, two white sheets, a small towel and a pillow as hard as a stone. I bring with me a suitcase with some clothing, some Buddhist books, a Greek-English dictionary and a battery-operated typewriter. I may be away for as long as a year and these are my possessions. I like the simplicity, the feeling of surrender. I think of the monks and nuns with only their robes and bowls.

And yet so many attachments remain. I decide to visit other islands for a few weeks and reluctantly leave my typewriter behind. But I am careful to pack my fountain pen. I quickly run out of ink and find I have left all my ink cartridges behind. I am swept by a wave of sorrow so deep I have to smile when I look at what it is I am clinging to so fiercely.

Again and again I am aware of my attachment to beauty. To live inland this summer means letting go of living beside the azure sea. And even though it is only a few miles away and I visit each day, it is painful to let it go. I watch myself clinging to the sight of the bright bougainvillea spilling over the white-washed walls or the silvery light that flickers in the olive trees. The monks speak of the pain, the *dukkha* of trying to hold on to beauty. These are only feelings, I say to myself and watch them come and go. Tonight I look up and the crescent moon is almost setting at the top of the village road. It looks as if I could run quickly up the road and catch it in my arms before it disappears.

There are few books in English on the island and I run out of reading material. At first I panic. How will I get through the long days and nights without the escape of reading, of losing myself for hours in the pages of a novel. It is a familiar feeling for when I visit the monastery I bring no books with me. I find as the hours and days flow by I can feel my restlessness begin to grow still. And in its place there is a sense of surrender, of timelessness. I sit quietly with the realization that this present moment is enough.

There have been times when I have run to the monastery to escape from myself, from my restlessness and confusion. Here too there are times when I feel lost in a maze of thoughts and fears and doubts. But more and more I come to trust the refuge of meditation. I sit beneath the stars and feel my sense of self begin to dissolve. And finally there is only watching, only a deep peacefulness.

I keep feeling that my experiences are imperceptibly changing, that something has shifted within me. I walk along a narrow footpath with ancient stone walls on both sides. I look up and a donkey is approaching bearing a huge load of hay. There is no room for me to pass and the donkey man walks behind the huge load and cannot see me. I call out to him in Greek but he doesn't respond and soon the donkey is only a few feet away. I suddenly spot a laddered gate and scamper clumsily over it to safety. It is hard to say what subtle change has taken place but the sense of watching seems deeper. I see my fear and my awkward scurry and the blue of the sky and the ringing eternal silence.

A few weeks later I have another experience of a subtle shift. I am awakened one night by a deep ache in one of my toes. I wash it in cold water and examine it and climb back into bed. But a few moments later another toe has the same strange and painful ache. I fling back the sheet and find a bright orange centipede. I have never seen one before but somehow feel certain of its identity. I rush to the balcony and shake the sheet in the wind. And then I put cold water on my foot and sit down to patiently wait. I have heard these stings are very dangerous and I am not sure what to expect. In a few hours I was planning to travel to another island but I wonder now if my plans will have to change. As I sit quietly I am aware of watching the pain, watching the fear, but the feelings seem to flow by without my clinging to them. Perhaps it is aversion that is missing. For a little while I feel blessedly free of a sense of self. I soon realize my toes no longer hurt. I climb a bit warily back into bed and am soon asleep.

As the months of solitude continue, I find myself growing more sensitive, more vulnerable. My moods swing from a deep sadness to soaring joy. A harsh word or a warm smile, a letter bearing good news or bad creates a rush of feeling. I contemplate the eight Worldly Conditions: Success and Failure, Fame and Dishonor, Gain and Loss, Happiness and Pain. Whatever I am feeling becomes much simpler, becomes only a basic human condition. To watch the joyous feelings is more difficult. My impulse is to enter them completely. But more and more I remember to watch them, to allow them to arise and cease.

I become ill and even my experience of illness seems somehow strange and new. I am walking on a footpath to a distant beach when I notice that my nose is a bit clogged. I am seldom ill so I feel confident that this is just in response to some pollen. But as the hours and days go by I have the odd sensation of watching illness enter me . . . first my nose, then my throat and finally my lungs. I feel as if my vision is penetrating my body and seeing clearly within. During the weeks that follow, I am quite ill. I visit a doctor and receive antibiotics. But still the illness continues. A strong wind blows each day and I sit quietly on a protected terrace. I have run out of reading material. And the long footpath walks I usually take aren't possible in the wind. I feel that my sickness is teaching me patience. The hours flow by and I watch the sun climb higher in the sky. There is a ringing silence all around me.

And then slowly, almost imperceptibly, I feel the illness begin to depart. Day after day I can follow its slow exodus from my body until finally I am well. About a month has gone by. I have never experienced this kind of clarity before. I have never felt such stillness.

The opportunity to practice patience and equanimity seem ever-present here. Tonight I walk through the little lanes of my village to the grocery store. The village is a lovely one with gleaming white houses with blue shutters and small gardens. I go into a courtyard of a chapel and sit there on the wall. And for a moment I find the silence I have been searching for. Then suddenly there is a loud banging. I look up and a few feet away from me, on the other side of the wall, a man is beating a mattress with a large stick. I laugh and continue walking until I come to another chapel. Here the scent of jasmine fills the air and a gentle breeze blows. But as I sit down a portable telephone rings and a woman in a nearby garden begins talking loudly. A man walks by carrying a small goat in a plastic bag. Only its head pokes out and it gazes up at me and gives a pitiful loud bleat.

I rent a room by the sea for one night and am ashamed to watch my equanimity fade away. I learn there are five children staying in the adjoining room with their parents. They are still playing merrily at midnight when I would like to go to sleep. Instead I take a long beach walk and sit for a long time gazing at a sea of bright stars. When I return it is quite late and at last everything is quiet. But I am awakened in the middle of the night by a sound I don't recognize. I hear the children whispering and laughing and then a series of loud crashes. It sounds as if they have turned the room into a bowling lane. I call out a few times but there is no response. I even hit the wall and am rewarded with an instantly aching hand. I listen to the waves sweeping into shore and am lulled by the sound. And I listen to the crashes and watch my anger. Sleep seems impossible. I wonder what the monks would do in this situation and I realize it is the hour when they rise to meditate. I get up to gaze out of the window and calm myself. And then I find it is my own shutters that are unhooked and are banging loudly in the wind. I feel a cacophony of feelings, shame and lingering anger and foolishness.

In the following days I reflect on my response to sounds. I cherish the sigh of the wind and the sea. And I listen eagerly for the owl calling in the night or the hoarse sorrowful cry of the donkey. I respond with aversion to loud noises . . . the blare of music, motorbikes, cars, machines. And yet this is the way it is. How much simpler it would be to regard it all with equanimity, to let go of all my aversions. How much simpler to surrender to what is.

This small island is said to have 365 chapels. On the buses the Greek women cross themselves each time they pass one. Their hands are almost always moving in a graceful dance as they ride. Each mountain is topped with a monastery, and little chapels can be found along each footpath whether high in the mountains or beside the sea. Each is surrounded by a veranda and a low white wall. Their doors are left unlocked and their cool interiors offer a refuge for everyone. I often stop and go inside and light a candle. It seems an opportunity for mindfulness.

Today I visit a little chapel on top of a hill with a lovely view to the sea below. I climb a long white stairway past groves of olive trees where cattle are dozing in the shade. I go inside and light a candle. Usually I pause for a few moments to send *metta* to those I am thinking of. But today so many beloved faces flood into my mind that it seems hopeless to do anything but offer *metta* to all.

My love of this country is deep, yet as the months go by I keep having the quiet realization that it doesn't matter where I am. I have spent years moving between places and yet nothing changes. My fears and hopes and dreams come with me. There are no departures, no arrivals, no coming and no going, I heard a monk intone many years ago. The words have echoed within me ever since and my understanding of their truth seems to slowly grow.

Sitting on my balcony each evening, I find myself returning to a meditation I began many years ago at the monastery. I reflect on the Seven Factors of Enlightenment: Mindfulness, Investigation, Energy, Rapture, Serenity, Concentration and Equanimity. These are faculties that reside in each of us. I feel like a gardener nurturing and watering seedlings. I consider each one slowly until it leads me gently to the next. I feel my sense of self begin to drop away. And I am left with clarity and brightness.

When I open my eyes I feel a sense of wonder and gratitude for the teachings that are deepening and unfolding within me. The colors of the sky have darkened. The moon is almost full. Two bats dance in delicate flickering flight.

Singing My Heartbroken Songs

JIHAD

My uncle says again and again that he wants to die. He asks God to please take him. He is ninety-four years old and has taken a fall in an elevator. In the hospital he is in a state of deep confusion. He gazes at his wife of sixty years and asks her the name of her husband. He stares at his son and asks him his name.

Osama bin Laden sleeps in a cave deep in the mountains. His wives and children are sleeping beside him. What is he dreaming of.

The radio announces that the FBI has declared a likelihood of terrorist acts this weekend. More letters containing anthrax spore are received. All of our lives have changed. We are all falling from skyscraper windows. We are all burning.

What do you do to restore yourself during these heartsick times, Kenyth writes to me. But we are almost strangers and I haven't yet learned to speak truthfully to him. I answer his letter with half-truths. I tell him I walk the long sandy beaches. But I do not tell him about singing every song I can remember, letting my voice soar over the trees and into the sky.

Once I had five uncles. This one with his deep longing to die is the last.

It was about six weeks ago that my daughter called me early in the morning to tell me about the attacks on the Pentagon and the World Trade Center. She was in tears. I turn on the television as we talk and the screen bombards me with simultaneous images of horror. The suffering is unimaginable.

And now only weeks later I hear the lawsuits are beginning . . . against the Taliban, the owners of the World Trade Center, the airlines, against Osama bin Laden. And now only weeks later we are bombing Afghanistan. The peasants there are bewildered. What did we do, they want to know.

I run away to a nearby Buddhist monastery. It is a place of peace and refuge. The monks have no television, no radio. It is only through their many visitors that they hear the news. One of the monks has been a friend for many years. He tells me how burdened and heavy he has felt since the attacks. He says we must meet each moment with equanimity, with mindfulness. And to help whenever the opportunity arises. We are all aghast at this war our government is waging in response to attacks by a small group of individuals.

The nights at the monastery soothe me. Amidst these steep hills and deep forests, the stars look enormous. They cascade across the sky and touch the tops of the hills. The air is filled with the sound of crickets. We meditate at dawn and at sundown. And the monks chant long protection chants in Pali. During the mornings I join the others at their work. I find some old work clothes and ride in the back of a pickup truck up the steep winding road. We are painting varnish on the decks of the small cabins the monks live in. We work in silence, scraping the thick sap that has collected on the decks, sweeping away the pine needles and applying the varnish. It is peaceful to simply be in the present moment doing whatever work is needed.

I dream of a march to Washington, all of us pressing eastward across the country . . . on foot, on bicycles and wagons, in cars and buses and trains. The momentum keeps gathering until we are an endless caravan, all of us begging for peace, crying out for peace. We move across mountains and forests and plains. This is our *jihad.* This is the holy cause we will lay down our lives for.

When I return home from the monastery, I call for news of my uncle. He has been asking again and again to go home. And even though he still cannot walk, he is bundled into a car with a wheel chair and a nurse and taken to his home. The hope is that his agitation and unhappiness will lessen there. But he recognizes nothing. He stares blankly at the family that has gathered to welcome him. He stares at the familiar rooms. I want to go home, he finally says.

I walk along a stream and sing my heartbroken songs. I sing about peace and forgiveness. I sing about love and loneliness and longing.

Tonight I sit by the fire. I am reading a book about the holocaust. I am strangely comforted to realize there have been other times in history as dark and troubled as this one. And suddenly the light from a motion detector blazes on. I walk to the door and gaze out. There is a large skunk just outside the door, its fur so thick and dark that I catch my breath at its beauty.

I make a business call to Baltimore. I am hurriedly told to call back later in the week. The building is in the process of being evacuated because of an anthrax threat. This call touches my life so lightly. And still it sears. We are all being changed by what is happening . . . changed in ways we don't realize, in ways we don't understand.

New books on bin Laden and on the Taliban appear in bookstore windows. The city of Berkeley becomes the first city to call for an end to the bombing. The Green party protests the war we are waging. But any calls for peace are met with threats and hostility.

The lives of Muslims living in this country are suddenly filled with tension and fear. There are a few deaths and many threats. I dream that all of us don Islamic dress . . . beards and turbans and fezzes, tunics and robes and veils and scarves. All the streets of all the cities fill with robed figures until we are indistinguishable, until we are all one.

Each morning I fill the bird feeders outside my windows. Chickadees and nuthatches flit back and forth between them. Bright acorn woodpeckers come to feed. A jet-black raven walks ponderously across the deck to eat the fallen seeds. A covey of quail glide across the grass. Here in this small town on the west coast I am so far from the suffering. Yet even here amidst this serenity, I can hear the cries of pain.

Kenyth writes of feeling disorganized, of not being able to get anything done. Friends from Holland write that they are frightened to death. And today I receive another letter. This one is from my cousin Mary, a poet. We have been exchanging poems for many months now and the exchange brings joy to each of us. But the attacks have silenced us until now. She writes:

> . . . across a tremendous fearful country
> I'm pretending now
> to write a poem

I remember how eerie it felt to drive from my house into the village on September eleventh. Everything appeared to be proceeding normally. The post office workers were busy sorting the mail. At the grocery store, people were buying bread and fruit and milk.

Others were waiting in line to conduct their business at the bank. I walked down the main street and stood gazing out to sea. Gulls still circled the bluffs and waves washed into shore. I returned home feeling dizzy and confused. Nothing made sense. Nothing seemed real.

I dream I am in a concentration camp. All of my family is also there. So is everyone I know. I don't know where the boundaries of the camp are. Perhaps it encompasses the whole country. Perhaps it encompasses the world.

In a shop in town I talk to a man who just arrived from New York City. He tells me he sees the ruins of the towers each time he goes to work and how devastating the sight is. I respond that it must be good for him to be here, to see that the rest of the country is unharmed. But as I say the words I realize how wrong they are. For even here life is splintered and askew.

I take a walk in the forest and pause for awhile beside a rushing stream. One very tall and slender tree is swaying wildly. All the trees that surround it are perfectly still.

I dream that my daughter is three years old and suddenly dies. She wasn't ill and there seems to be no reason for her death. I am filled with sorrow, with an aching emptiness. I know I need to weep, to sob, to scream out my pain. But I cannot.

In the paper today there are photographs of the hijackers. As I stare at them, I notice how young and innocent they look. Now it is believed that many of them were told the hijackings would be ordinary ones. They did not know they were about to die. And there is a photograph of bin Laden I've never seen before. He looks like a priest in his flowing white robe. Who is this man who speaks like a poet and warns that the storm in the sky will continue. Who is this man who fulfills his father's prophecy that one of his sons will fight against the enemies of Islam.

I take a trip to the Florida Keys. I have been planning this trip for a long time. And though I thought of canceling it, something in me wants to be traveling, to see what airports are like now, to feel the mood of the country. I take a red-eye flight and the airport is quiet. My body is checked very gently by a woman who asks permission to touch me. National Guardsmen with their rifles stand watching.

When I reach the Keys I check into a guesthouse. I rent a bicycle and take long rides around the island. I wander the harbor and the bookstores and the beaches. When I read the local newspapers I learn that there are a series of anthrax scares happening here. And I learn that the suspension bridges in California have been threatened.

I visit a beautiful garden and gaze at almond trees and banyan trees, and pandaris or walking pines whose many branches root themselves into the ground. The weather is sultry and windy and humid. A depression has formed which may build into a hurricane.

And a few days later a hurricane has developed. It quickly builds in strength and appears to be heading straight for the Keys. A mandatory evacuation is issued. The guesthouse staff insists that I leave. I ask around about the possibilities of staying on. I even find an inn that will allow me to stay if I sign a responsibility waiver. But it turns out that the staff plans on evacuating and I would probably be alone. I have been told there is a good chance of a loss of power and water. Even food could be difficult to find. I sadly make plans to depart. I take a last bicycle ride, watching all the houses and resorts get boarded up. The humidity is building and so is the wind. By evening only a few restaurants are still open and I am alone in my guesthouse. When I depart at dawn, the town looks bleak and deserted.

When I finally reach home, a quiet shift seems to have taken place. No one seems to be talking about the war now. Even the newspapers have made room for other subjects. Today there is a front page story about new regulations for toppings on frozen pizza. Yet still our bombs continue to explode and Afghanis are dying. I want to plead with everyone that we must not allow ourselves to grow numb, that we must keep our hearts open. But I cannot find the words.

Later in the day I receive news that my uncle has died. His last few hours were peaceful ones.

I drive north to my favorite beach. I walk along and watch the waves crest and then tumble into shore. The sea is very rough and the sky is gray. I try to sing but all the songs have disappeared.

RAMADAN

The holy month of *Ramadan* begins today. We are at war with a nation at prayer.

I take a long walk on the bluffs. It is a cloudy day and the sea has black shadows. Kelp washes in and out with the waves.

Mullah Mohammed Omar, the Taliban supreme leader, says there are plans to destroy America. The real matter, he says, is the extinction of America. And, God willing, it will fall to the ground. He believes this will happen soon.

As I drive home at twilight I come to a large buck standing beside the road. I stop and gaze at him. He is almost close enough to

277

touch. He averts his eyes and freezes there in the fading light. I sit beside him for a long time and finally drive slowly on.

Tonight there are meteor showers called the Leonids. Astronomers say this should be the finest display in our lifetime. I wake in the middle of the night and go outside wrapped in a warm quilt. Meteors streak across the sky leaving long bright trails. The whole night is ablaze. I wonder if this is the way a war-torn sky looks. I sit there in the cold and the silence watching a dance of light.

I go to spend a few days at the monastery. I walk the steep trails stopping now and then to run my hands over the cool smooth bark of manzanita. Bright autumn leaves lie scattered on the ground. The air is silent. Now and then my passage disturbs a bird and I hear a ruffle of wings among the leaves. Clouds mass overhead and the day is gray and misty.

A few hours later the rains begin. To go out for a moment, even with an umbrella, is to get wet. There is no overhang outside the meditation hall so I leave my shoes on the porch of the house, remove my socks and walk barefoot to the hall. The distance is only a few steps and walking on the cold wet pavement feels good.

I sit in a small trailer and look out at the rain falling ceaselessly. An oak tree stretches its crooked arms to the sky. Fog drifts over the hills. The steady rain on the metal roof washes away my thoughts. This is the first time I have stayed in this trailer. But I feel as if I have always lived here. The bed is piled high with quilts. My daypack is slung over a hook and my journal and books are on a shelf. Outside, rain rushes down the steep hills.

It is Thanksgiving and I have brought a few pies to the monastery. Others have also brought special dishes for the meal. The monks have only one meal a day at 10:30 a.m. I help out in the kitchen peeling hot chestnuts, grating cheeses and slicing pies. About six of us are helping out in the small kitchen and there is a feeling of warm camaraderie. At last everything is ready and the table is brimming with food. The monks fill their wooden bowls and chant a blessing in Pali. And then the rest of us fill our bowls and sit cross-legged on the floor. The meal takes place in silence.

I take a long walk before I leave. The stream beds have been dry for many months. Now bright water rushes and spills over the rocks. The air is filled with its singing.

This is the sacred month of *Ramadan*. The Koran instructs that one can eat and drink only until it is possible to tell a white thread from a black one in the light of the coming dawn. From sunup until sundown neither food nor water are taken.

I have been coughing now for month after month. My doctor has made me an appointment to have some tests at the hospital. I breathe in and out while strange machines make their measurements. The technician who assists me is so kind that I hug her when I leave.

I call my aunt. Since my uncle has died I think of her often. We chat for awhile. I have been telephoning frequently. I wish there was something I could do to erase her pain.

Life has a shattered feeling. Here in this small community we no longer talk about the bombs falling on Afghanistan. We do not talk about the plans for secret trials by military tribunals for suspected terrorists. It is not that we have grown indifferent. But there seem to be no words left to say.

I run into a friend who is a reporter for a local newspaper. People are driving differently, she tells me. There are many more accidents now.

The day is bright with sunlight. I walk down to the beach. A car is parked there with a man sitting inside. Something about him catches my eye and I find myself checking to see if he is holding a rifle. The thought feels totally foreign. It feels as if it belongs to someone else.

One of the headlines today is, America Is Number One In The World For Sex. The article describes a study done by a condom manufacturer. Just beside it is an article entitled, World Pooling Its Efforts In Terror War.

I dream of leaving the country to wander from place to place. I dream of becoming a nomad, a gypsy, a pilgrim. But there is nowhere left to go.

There is a small earthquake a few miles offshore. The days teeter between storms and dazzling sunshine. Waves send their wild white spray cascading high above the rocks. The bird feeders are a flurry of activity. Acorn woodpeckers appear with their fluffy scarlet caps. The lawn is filled with flickers and robins. Scrub jays and gray jays wait on the fenceposts. Nuthatches flit by.

Cascades of rain tumble down. Lightning streaks across the sky. The wind tosses the branches of the firs. A fawn tiptoes between trees. I load up the wheelbarrow again and again and stack firewood by the door.

I dress warmly and walk the beach. Broken sand dollars lie scattered in the sand. Necklaces of yellow kelp lie in tangles. A cold wind blows. It begins to rain.

I receive a letter from Kenyth. He too is undergoing medical tests. He speaks of the dread thoughts he is keeping at bay. They are like a storm threatening to race in, he says. I feel the same way as I wait for the doctor to call me about my own test results. Our letters are drawing us closer. I will be taking a trip in a few weeks and will be near the city where he lives. We make plans to see each other.

The Taliban is surrendering in city after city. Our bombs continue to fall. And now there are news articles about the focus of war shifting soon. Our government is learning more about terrorist networks in the Philippines, Indonesia, Somalia and Yemen.

This is the sacred month of *Ramadan,* the month of fasting. The long fast is a way to share the experiences of those who are poor, of those who are hungry. It is a way to learn humility. This is a time to show kindness, to show compassion. This is a time to make amends.

I drive to town to get the mail and do a few errands. When I return I find my door has blown open. And awhile later as I lie reading by the fire, some movement catches my eye. I see a very small animal cross the room and enter the bedroom. I follow after it and find a frightened chipmunk hiding behind the dresser. I am puzzled about what I should do. I know I don't want the chipmunk to be imprisoned inside without any food. I open the bedroom window hoping it will find the way out. And I prepare a saucer of treats— two piles of ten sunflower seeds, two grapes cut in half, and a walnut broken into four pieces. By knowing the exact amounts of the food, I am hoping to keep track of whether the chipmunk is still inside. I also borrow a live trap and place some rolled oats inside. I know chipmunks hibernate in winter. I am hoping this one doesn't tunnel into a corner of the closet. I have a feeling it would be much cozier and happier in a tunnel in the damp rich earth.

Kenyth calls to plan our meeting. He has received his test results and they are negative. And I have just had a call from my doctor that my results are good. Entering the medical world is like approaching a vast abyss. It is the first time I have been close enough to the edge to peer in and see how bottomless it is. But for now we have both been reprieved.

I drive over to visit a friend in the next town. Her meadow is filled with wild turkeys. They sit along the top of the fence side by side. They walk in the meadow. A group of deer are also there grazing serenely. We walk up for a closer look and neither the turkeys nor the deer move away.

A deadline for surrender is announced but no one comes forward. The air strikes continue relentlessly. Bin Laden is believed to be somewhere deep within the Tora Bora caves.

I walk down to the mouth of the river. It has changed its course and the sand flats I walked on a few days ago have mysteriously disappeared. The hills cast reflections in the green translucent water. Beneath each gull afloat on the river, another gull ripples.

I receive a letter from a friend who is in her eighties. She has just won a twenty-five thousand dollar award for her paintings, her second award this year. She has also had several museum shows in the last few months. It is a joy to see her receiving so much acclaim. Now I have money to fix my leaking roof, she writes.

I go to a film about South Africa's Truth and Reconciliation Commission. It awakens my hope. It awakens a dream of America embracing a system of restorative justice, one that helps to heal its own wounds and the wounds of its enemies. I imagine hatred and violence and bitterness melting away. I dare to imagine peace.

The new moon appears in the sky marking the end of the holy month of *Ramadan*. A three day festival, *Eid al-Fitr,* follows. This is a time of food and gifts and prayer. This is a time of joy and thanksgiving.

FORGIVENESS

Why do you write, Kenyth asks in a letter. I write to be forgiven, I answer. It is the only answer that I know.

Bombs continue to thunder on Tora Bora day and night. This is the time of the festival *Eid al-Fitr.* Fireworks dance into the air and music plays.

Today when I walk into the wind I shiver with cold. When I turn to walk the other way, it feels like spring. The bluffs are filled with meadowlarks, their yellow breasts brightening the day.

Bin Laden has so far eluded his pursuers. There are rumors that he is being transformed by plastic surgeons. There are rumors he has slipped over the border into Pakistan. There are rumors that he has been killed.

I buy a small glass hummingbird for Kenyth. I am hoping he will hang it in his window to remind him the light will be returning. I will be leaving in the morning on a trip to the northwest and we have plans to meet for a few hours.

I turn on the radio in the evening to a program that is providing brief summaries of the news from other countries in the world. Kofi Annan, the news broadcaster says, has forbidden the United States to extend its war on terrorism to other countries. It is Iraq and Somalia in particular that he is concerned about. My heart lifts for a moment. But I have grave doubts that our newspapers will print such a statement. For the next few days I search the papers eagerly and find nothing. Still I go on hoping it is true, hoping he will continue to speak out for peace until his voice rings everywhere.

I get to the airport hours before my flight. The security line is very long. After my body is thoroughly checked, I am asked to remove my boots so they can be put through the x-ray machine. The whole airport with its armed guards is a grim reminder that we are at war. By the time I am able to reach my gate, the plane is already boarding.

I read that Iraq, Somalia, Sudan, Iran, Yemen and Syria are all countries the United States might turn to next in its war on terror. I shudder to see the list of enemies grow longer. I read of more Afghani villages that have been bombed by accident. And I read that the entire leadership of the Taliban has survived the bombing and eluded capture. Many have quietly melted back into their own tribes.

When I arrive in Washington, I visit a friend on an island where I used to live. Bald eagles soar overhead. The yacht harbor is bright with flickering Christmas lights and ferries come and go.

I find a New York Times article quoting Kofi Annan. He says that expanding the war on terrorism into Iraq would only increase tensions in the Middle East. This is a much milder statement than the one I heard on the radio. But still I am glad to find it.

The president is deciding what to do about John Walker. This young American who joined the Taliban could be simply stripped of citizenship, but he could also be given a military court martial or charged with treason. It is possible he could be executed. The former president Bush has suggested, "Make him leave his hair the way it is and his face as dirty as it is and let him go wandering around this country and see what kind of sympathy he would get."

I buy a few last Christmas presents in the island shops. And I walk along the beach. The afternoon grows very cold. A slender moon appears in the sky.

An Iraqi defector describes his work on biological, chemical and nuclear weapons. I grow afraid this is the prelude to extending the war into Iraq.

I look at houses for sale on the island dreaming of finding one to buy. There is a house on a mountain looking out to sea, a house in a wide green meadow, a cabin in the forest. I am staying at my friend's house. Outside her windows is a large pond. We sit and talk and watch the wind rippling the water. The tall trees cast their reflections. A few ducks swim past.

Early in the morning I board the ferry to return to the mainland. The dawn has turned the sky a deep pink. Then one by one the islands are lit with sunlight. Snow-capped mountains touch the sky. The ferry weaves among islands. Kenyth will be meeting me and driving me to Seattle where my son and his family live.

Are you nervous, Kenyth asks me. We haven't seen each other in about five months. And even then we only spent a few hours together. I could easily be nervous but I'm not. The only feeling I am aware of is a pure gladness. We meander slowly south, taking beautiful back roads that weave along the water. We park for a long time at a beach and sit there talking and watching the waves wash in. And then we reluctantly continue on our way to Seattle where we must say goodbye.

I am spending a week with my son and his wife and my two little granddaughters. The younger one is still in her first year. I see her suddenly stand by herself for the first time. She beams proudly and claps her hands. And then she collapses to a sitting position. And then she stands again and again, teetering precariously and grinning.

Her older sister is almost three. She has always been shy with me. But this time we grow closer. We walk together holding hands and we brush each other's hair. We sit side by side at a small table and have a tea party with tiny cups.

I take a walk down to the locks. The sun glistens. It has been raining here for weeks and everyone is out rejoicing in the warm sunshine, watching the boats waiting to go through the locks. I speak to a man who describes the beauty of the spawning salmon that arrive in the summer. They leap, he says, to celebrate life. And then they die.

A young man flying from Paris to Miami is caught and subdued as he tries to detonate a bomb he has concealed in his shoe. If he hadn't been stopped, the explosives were powerful enough to blow a hole in the plane.

On Christmas morning we go for a long walk in the cold clear air. And in the evening we drive to a neighbor's house that is elaborately decorated. A crowd has gathered to watch reindeer nodding their heads, streams of bubbles floating into the night, blinking lights and santas and dancing elves.

On my last night I pat my smallest granddaughter as she is falling asleep in her crib. And then I sit in a rocker in the darkened room and watch her. Her head rests on a small stuffed dog that I brought her. For a long time she lies with her eyes open, in some mysterious place between waking and sleep. And finally her eyes close. I continue to sit there for a long time.

When I arrive home I find a letter from my cousin Mary. She has enclosed a poem, the first she has written since just after the attacks. It is a poem full of pain that she wrote quickly and mailed quickly before she could allow herself to judge it or dismiss it. The poem describes how horrible it is to read the news each day.

All the bird feeders are empty and I fill them with sunflower seeds. I put out a cake of suet for the acorn woodpeckers and the nuthatches and chickadees.

A new video of Osama bin Laden is made public. He looks very gaunt and ill and his beard has grown white. It has long been rumored that he is suffering from kidney disease and now doctors are speculating that without medication he may be dying. And in the tape he refers to his own death. All along he has claimed he was not responsible for the September eleventh attacks. And now he says that it is inconceivable that his followers would go after innocent civilians. He goes on to say that the hijackers were only high school students. And he likens the bombs the United States is dropping on Afghanistan to terrorism.

The world is still reeling. The world is still shattering into pieces. The new government in Afghanistan is established and feels it is time for our bombing to stop. Yet the headlines read, U.S. Forces Facing Long Afghan Stay. I read an article by a Buddhist teacher about deep listening and our need to learn to hear one another. It is our only hope for peace. And then I read that the president has only heard a snippet of the bin Laden video and has no intention of hearing more. Plans continue to put terrorist suspects before military tribunals. Pakistan and India prepare to go to war.

More and more I seem to have difficulty separating myself from other people. All the lines of demarcation seem to be dissolving. I wonder if it is Buddhist meditation that has caused this blurring of boundaries.

I think of Osama bin Laden, thin and ill now and perhaps close to death. And I think of his wives and his children. I think of the young hijackers who may not have known they were about to die a violent death. I think of all the Americans who have lost their children or their fathers or their mothers or their friends. And all the Afghanis who are starving, who are dying. All the terror and all the suffering, all the tears and hopes and dreams are merging, are blending. What can we do but forgive one another or die.

Judith Azrael was born in Baltimore, Maryland. She is a graduate of the University of Wisconsin and holds an MFA from the University of Oregon. She has taught writing workshops at art centers and colleges and has been a Visiting Writer at Western Washington University. She has published four books of poetry: *Fire in August* (Zeitgeist Press), *Fields of Light* (Cassiopeia Press), and *Antelope are Running* and *Apple Tree Poems* (both from Confluence Press). Her poetry, fiction and lyrical essays have appeared in anthologies and numerous magazines, including *Atlanta Review, Harvard Review, The Minnesota Review, The Nation, Poets & Writers Magazine, Rosebud, Shenandoah, The Sun, Western Humanities Review* and *The Yale Review*. For many years she has moved between a seaside village in Northern California and the islands of Puget Sound and currently lives on San Juan Island. She has two children and two small grandchildren. She travels to Greece whenever she can and is now working on a full-length book set in the Greek islands.